THIN ICE

■ A POETRY ANTHOLOGY ■
EDITED BY DAVID KITCHEN

OXFORD UNIVERSITY PRESS 1991

Oxford University Press, Walton Street, Oxford OX2 6DP

Oxford New York Toronto
Delhi Bombay Calcutta Madras Karachi
Petaling Jaya Singapore Hong Kong Tokyo
Nairobi Dar es Salaam Cape Town
Melbourne Auckland

and associated companies in
Berlin Ibadan

Oxford is a trade mark of Oxford University Press

Selection, arrangement and editorial matter © David Kitchen 1991

Published by Oxford University Press 1991

All rights reserved. This publication may not be reproduced, stored or transmitted, in any forms or by any means, except in accordance with the terms of licences issued by the Copyright Licensing Agency, or except for fair dealing for the purposes of research or private study, or criticism or review, as permitted under the Copyright, Designs and Patents Act, 1988. Enquiries concerning reproduction outside these terms should be addressed to the Permissions Department, Oxford University Press.

A CIP catalogue record for this book is available from the British Library.

ISBN 0 19 833183 5

Typeset by Pentacor PLC, High Wycombe, Bucks
Printed in Great Britain by
Billing & Sons Ltd, Worcester

Contents

3

Part Three *To Be Continued*

Introduction

It is now six years since I began to work with English groups on the courses that led to a single examining system at sixteen plus for most pupils. From the beginning I was exercised by the challenge of whether it was possible to provide a satisfactory poetry anthology that would be accessible to all pupils but would stretch the most able. This book has not taken six years to make but it has only been relatively recently that I felt enough pupils had steered their way through the system for me to have a clear idea of what might fit the purpose.

This anthology is built around the recognition that talking and writing about poetry is helped a great deal by contrast. The first part consists of paired poems and the second, thematic, part provides further opportunities to place one poem alongside another in discussion and debate. It is my hope that working in this way will assist the encouraging movement away from seeing an individual poem in isolation.

Except for the briefest of thoughts at the opening of each section, the suggestions about how pupils might respond are kept for the final part of the book. To Be Continued does not attempt to cover the whole range of possible responses: that is one reason for its title. In particular, it leaves to the teacher the task of focusing upon individual lines, phrases and constructions. To attempt that in cold print would be to produce something clumsy, prescriptive and unrelated to the highly unpredictable results of group discussion. What the final part of the book does attempt to do is to provide a selection of ideas and ways in which poetry may be explored. A balance has been sought between ideas that relate to specific poems and the more general suggestions that might be used in a variety of contexts.

Poetry is a little like skating on thin ice: it can be exciting when all is going well but there is the ever-present danger of the icy waters of negative response. This book will not always remove the icy waters but it is hoped that it will, at least, make the skating as exhilarating and as varied as possible.

David Kitchen

Part One
Contrasts

Contrasts

Sometimes I try to find a title that would fit both poems. That can be more difficult than it sounds.

I'm never too sure how I feel about a poem unless I can compare it with another one.

A Knock at the Door

                                    You open the door
And you step back
From a sheltering bulk. A tumblesky wet January
Mid-morning. Close, tall, in-leaning
Hairiness of a creature, darkness of a person –

A bristling of wet-rotten woods, mould-neglect, night-weather,
A hurt wildness stands there for help
And is saying something. Wild lumpy coat,
Greasy face-folds and sly eyes and a bandit abruptness,
Speech nearly not speech
Ducking under speech, asking for money
As if not asking. Huge storm-sky strangeness

And desperation. He knows he stands
In a shatter of your expectations. He waits for you
To feel through to his being alive.
He wants to flee. His cornered wildness
Dodges about in his eyes
That try to hide inside themselves, and his head jerks up
Trying to fit back together odd bits of dignity,
And he goes on, muttering, nodding, signalling OK OK.

Till you register: Money.

You give him bread, plastered with butter and piled with
    marmalade,
And stand watching him cram it into his mouth –
His wet, red, agile mouth
In the swollen collapsed face.
His grimed forefinger cocked.
A black column of frayed coat, belted with string,
Has surfaced for help.
Stares into the house-depth past you
Stranger than a snow-covered starving stag.
Munches, wipes his fingers on his coat, and wipes his mouth
With the black-creased red palm.
A smile works his rubbery face
Like a hand working into a big glove.
His eyes wobble at you
Then an assault of launched eloquence

Like a sudden flooding of gratitude –
But you can't decode it.
He is extricating from his ponderous coat a topless bean-can.
Spot o' tea in this ere, surr, if it's possible –

A prayer to be invisible,
Eyes flickering towards the road as if casually
He dips his lips to the scalding can's metal and sucks
Coolingly, hurriedly,
And now it comes again (the tossed-empty can back in his
    pocket)
In a slither of thanks and salutes and shoulder-squarings
And sparring, feinting, dagger-stab glances
From the dissolved blue eyes
And the cornered mouse panic trying to slip into the house past
    you –

MONEY!

Anaesthetic for the big body,
Its glistening full veins, its pumping organs,
Its great nerves to the eyes,
Unmanageable parcel of baggy pain
With its dry-sore brains, its tied rawness –

You give him your pocketful and he buries it without a glance
And he's gone
Under his shoulder hunch, with hiding hands
And feet pretending no hurry
Under spattering and sneezing trees, over shining cobbles
To fall within two hundred yards
Dead-drunk in the church, to lie
Blowing, as if in post-operational shock,
Abandoned to space,
A lolling polyp of sweaty life, wrapped in its Guy Fawkes rags,
Bristling face-patch awry.

Ted Hughes

13

An Old Woman

An old woman grabs
hold of your sleeve
and tags along.

She wants a fifty paise coin.
She says she will take you
to the horseshoe shrine.

You've seen it already.
She hobbles along anyway
and tightens her grip on your shirt.

She won't let you go.
You know how old women are.
They stick to you like burr.

You turn around and face her
with an air of finality.
You want to end the farce.

When you hear her say,
'What else can an old woman do
on hills as wretched as these?'

You look right at the sky.
Clear through the bullet holes
she has for her eyes.

And as you look on,
the cracks that begin around her eyes
spread beyond her skin.

And the hills crack.
And the temples crack.
And the sky falls

with a plateglass clatter
around the shatterproof crone
who stands alone.

And you are reduced
to so much small change
in her hand.

Arun Kolatkar

The Lake

For years there have been no fish in the lake.
People hurrying through the park avoid it
like the plague. Birds steer clear
and the sedge of course has withered.
Trees lean away from it,
and at night it reflects, not the moon,
but the blackness of its own depths.
There are no fish in the lake.
But there is life there. There is life . . .

Underwater pigs glide between reefs of coral debris.
They love it here. They breed and multiply
in sties hollowed out of the mud
and lined with mattresses and bedsprings.
They live on dead fish and rotting things,
drowned pets, plastic and assorted excreta.
Rusty cans they like the best.
Holding them in webbed trotters
their teeth tear easily through the tin,
and poking in a snout, they noisily suck out
the putrid matter within.

There are no fish in the lake.
But there is life there. There is life . . .

For on certain evenings after dark
shoals of pigs surface
and look out at those houses near the park.
Where, in bathrooms,
children feed stale bread to plastic ducks,
and in attics,
toy yachts have long since run aground.
Where, in livingrooms,
anglers dangle their lines on patterned carpets,
and bemoan the fate of the ones that got away.

Down on the lake, piggy eyes glisten.
They have acquired a taste for flesh.
They are licking their lips. Listen . . .

Roger McGough

The Newcomer

'There's something new in the river,'
The fish said as it swam –
'It's got no scales, no fins and no gills,
And ignores the impassable dam.'

'There's something new in the trees,'
I heard a bloated thrush sing,
'It's got no beak, no claws, and no feathers,
And not even the ghost of a wing.'

'There's something new in the warren,'
Said the rabbit to the doe.
'It's got no fur, no eyes and no paws,
Yet digs deeper than we dare go.'

'There's something new in the whiteness,'
Said the snow-bright polar bear.
'I saw its shadow on a glacier,
But it left no pawmarks there.'

Through the animal kingdom
The news was spreading fast –
No beak, no claws, no feather,
No scales, no fur, no gills,
It lives in the trees and the water,
In the soil and the snow and the hills,
And it kills and it kills and it kills.

Brian Patten

The Contract

They offered me a contract when my turn came to be born,
A water-tight agreement, all well and truly drawn:
The guarantee on parchment with a flourish six-inch long
And a great fat gob of sealing-wax as big as any gong –
    But I didn't read the small print at the bottom.

A free land to live in and God's free air to breathe;
Free milk, free specs, free dentures before I'd lost my teeth;
A free education in grammar school or college,
And a free encyclopaedia to the whole of modern knowledge –
    But I didn't read the small print at the bottom.

A Five-Star Mental Clinic with free soap for blowing bubbles
And psychologists in every room to listen to my troubles;
A gold ring for my finger, for my mouth, a silver spoon,
And a ticket for a non-return excursion to the moon –
    But I didn't read the small print at the bottom.

I was analysed and treated with a mild electric shock.
They brought me here by rocket and took back a lump of rock;
Gave me a litre of oxygen and left me on my own
Playing marbles with the polished glassy pebbles of the moon –
    'Cause I hadn't read the small print at the bottom.

Oh, they carried out their promises, said what they had to say.
For however free your life is, you've always got to pay.
You sign along the dotted line and your name's stamped out in
    black!
You're born into a one-way street and there's no turning back –
    So always read the small print at the bottom.

Norman Nicholson

A Consumer's Report

The name of the product I tested is *Life*,
I have completed the form you sent me
and understand that my answers are confidential.
I had it as a gift,
I didn't feel much while using it,
in fact I think I'd have liked to be more excited.
It seemed gentle on the hands
but left an embarrassing deposit behind.
It was not economical
and I have used much more than I thought
(I suppose I have about half left
but it's difficult to tell) –
although the instructions are fairly large
there are so many of them
I don't know which to follow, especially
as they seem to contradict each other.
I'm not sure such a thing
should be put in the way of children –
It's difficult to think of a purpose
for it. One of my friends says
it's just to keep its maker in a job.
Also the price is much too high.
Things are piling up so fast,
after all, the world got by
for a thousand million years
without this, do we need it now?
(Incidentally, please ask your man
to stop calling me 'the respondent',
I don't like the sound of it.)
There seems to be a lot of different labels,
sizes and colours should be uniform,
the shape is awkward, it's waterproof
but not heat resistant, it doesn't keep
yet it's very difficult to get rid of:
whenever they make it cheaper they seem
to put less in – if you say you don't
want it, then it's delivered anyway.
I'd agree it's a popular product,

it's got into the language; people
even say they're on the side of it.
Personally I think it's overdone,
a small thing people are ready
to behave badly about. I think
we should take it for granted. If its
experts are called philosophers or market
researchers or historians, we shouldn't
care. We are the consumers and the last
law makers. So finally, I'd buy it.
But the question of a 'best buy'
I'd like to leave until I get
the competitive product you said you'd send.

Peter Porter

I Had a Strange Dream

I had a strange dream last night:
I was to be shot at dawn.
I was imprisoned in a concrete basement
From which the dawn was not visible.
And then one of my classmates appeared,
We used to sit together at the same desk,
Copying out exercises from each other
And throwing a paper dart
(For some reason it wouldn't fly).
My classmate said: 'Good evening.
How unlucky you've been. I'm very sorry.
I mean, being shot – it's so inhumane.
I've always believed in soft measures.
But somehow no one asked me,
They just gave me a pistol and sent me.
I'm not here alone, you know, my family's here,
I've got a wife and kids – a son and daughter.
Look, I can show you their photographs.
My daughter's like me, don't you think?
You see, I've got an old mother.
I mustn't put her health at risk.
The council gave us a new flat just recently,
It's got a pink-tiled bathroom.
And my wife wants a washing machine.
I mean, I can't . . . Anyway, it's no good . . .
There's nothing we can do to change things.
I've a pass to go to the Crimea, to a sanatorium.
They'll shoot you at dawn all the same.
If they hadn't sent me, it'd have been another.
Perhaps somebody you didn't know.
And after all we did go to school together.
And throw paper darts together.
You've just no idea how bad
It makes me feel, but what can you do?'

Irina Ratushinskaya

I Sit and Look Out

I sit and look out upon all the sorrows of the world, and upon
    all oppression and shame,
I hear secret convulsive sobs from young men at anguish with
    themselves, remorseful after deeds done,
I see in low life the mother misused by her children, dying,
    neglected, gaunt, desperate,
I see the wife misused by her husband, I see the treacherous
    seducer of young women,
I mark the ranklings of jealousy and unrequited love attempted
    to be hid, I see these sights on the earth,
I see the working of battle, pestilence, tyranny, I see martyrs
    and prisoners,
I observe a famine at sea, I observe the sailors casting lots who
    shall be kill'd to preserve the lives of the rest,
I observe the slights and degradations cast by arrogant persons
    upon laborers, the poor, and upon negroes, and the like;
All these – all the meanness and agony without end I sitting
    look out upon,
See, hear, and am silent.

Walt Whitman

The Collier

When I was born on Amman hill
A dark bird crossed the sun.
Sharp on the floor the shadow fell;
I was the youngest son.

And when I went to the County School
I worked in a shaft of light.
In the wood of the desk I cut my name:
Dai for Dynamite.

The tall black hills my brothers stood;
Their lessons all were done.
From the door of the school when I ran out
They frowned to watch me run.

The slow grey bells they rung a chime
Surly with grief or age.
Clever or clumsy, lad or lout,
All would look for a wage.

I learnt the valley flowers' names
And the rough bark knew my knees.
I brought home trout from the river
And spotted eggs from the trees.

A coloured coat I was given to wear
Where the lights of the rough land shone.
Still jealous of my favour
The tall black hills looked on.

They dipped my coat in the blood of a kid
And they cast me down a pit,
And although I crossed with strangers
There was no way up from it.

Soon as I went from the County School
I worked in a shaft. Said Jim,
'You will get your chain of gold, my lad,
But not for a likely time.'

And one said, 'Jack was not raised up
When the wind blew out the light
Though he interpreted their dreams
And guessed their fears by night.'

And Tom, he shivered his leper's lamp
For the stain that round him grew;
And I heard mouths pray in the after-damp
When the picks would not break through.

They changed words there in darkness
And still through my head they run,
And white on my limbs is the linen sheet
And gold on my neck the sun.

Vernon Watkins

Saturday Sailor

There was once a man, a bit of a Saturday sailor,
Man called Noah, down by the children's pond
Every Saturday afternoon, with his Cutty Sark,
Radio-controlled Mayflower and, pride of the fleet,
A three-foot aircraft carrier built from sardine tins,
And the voice said: 'See you're a bit of a sailor, Noah,
I'd like you to build me something,' and Noah said:
'Only in a minor way, just mess about, you know.'
And the voice said: 'I know that, I watch you
Heating up the solder, reading "Jane's Fighting Ships"
While your wife's at bingo, when your son's stopped asking
For help with homework and your daughter's saving
To leave home.' Noah protested: 'They drove me to it,
They've no interest in me, they loathe ships.'
And the voice said: 'They'll learn to live with it,
Now this boat I want . . . ' Noah said: 'I'm no good
Making rowing-boats, I've tried,' and the voice said:
'Oh, it's a bit bigger than that.' 'I'm no good
With yachts, even the model ones go wrong.'

– 'That's not quite what I was thinking of.'
Then Noah said: 'Why are you picking on me,
It's not my fault the family's split, take Michael
He's always got his head in books, mad on animals,'
And the voice said: 'I know, I need someone good
With rabbits and guinea-pigs, and bison and things . . .'
Noah slammed Full Steam Astern, rammed Cutty Sark
Amidships with Ark Royal, they bubbled to the bottom
Of the children's pond and the voice said:
'That has to be my world, the rest you will take
With you, your boat will dwarf the local bank,
The housing estate, will overshadow the church;
Your cargo will be two of all my creatures:
And this is in your hand.' And the water rippled
And the ducks clattered and the trees sighed
And everything was very quiet by the children's pond,
Because the children had all gone home,
Obedient to suburban parents who had told them:
'Never stay near to men who talk to themselves,'
And clouds were rearing up, threatening some rain.

Martyn Halsall

Gangrene

They brought a boy to me, twelve years old,
his arm wrapped up in dirty bandages,
a quiet, well-mannered boy, who smiled
shyly when I tickled him under the chin.
He was from my ancestral village, the son
of a carpenter who was a cousin-by-marriage
of a tanner I traded with. It was, therefore,
natural they should come to me for help.

The story was simply this: The boy had fallen
from the roof while flying a kite. The damage
was negligible, just a shattered elbow.
From that height he could have very well
broken his neck. It was a miracle considering
he fell on a brick-pile. I looked at the boy.
He seemed quite modest about his achievement.
Or, perhaps, he was still thinking of the lost kite.

The only mender of bones in a village
is the local wrestler. They showed him the arm,
and without so much as a second glance
he got busy with oil and lint. It is truly
a miracle, he said, the boy could have broken
his neck. This is nothing but a fracture.
After pocketing the money, he patted the boy
on the head, and sent them away happy.

But the bone was stubborn, it refused to mend.
This is more serious than I thought, said the
wrestler. However, there is nothing to worry about.
In four or five days he will be running around
as good as new. So he set it again,
and scolded the boy for showing so much pain.
He pocketed the money. Satisfied, the relatives
went home. But the bone did not mend.

This much they told me. I guessed the rest.
The days of growing anxiety; the wrestler's refusal
to admit his mistake; the unlimited optimism
of the parents. But when the limb blackened and began

to stink, they got frightened. They could sense
the fear in the wrestler too, though he insisted
it would be all right. The boy is in the power
of a djinn, he said. But he could not hide his fear.

So here they were, too late as usual, come at last
to their only contact in the city. I could not stand
the animal appeal in their eyes. My proximity
to the mission hospital was surely a passport
to personal attention. I changed quickly
and went with them. The mission surgeon, a greedy
tactless butcher, took one perfunctory look.
Gangrene, he said in English, the arm must come off.

In this case he was right, of course. I had
already guessed by the smell. Still, my heart
sank when I looked at the boy; he was watching
a flock of pigeons in the courtyard. How shall
I tell them? I thought, how shall I tell them?
In the end I did not have to. The tanner guessed
by my face. Tactfully, he took me aside.
I told him. He then went and talked to the father.

I have never seen anybody so indignant.
Instead of grief there was only anger, or
the anger was because of the grief. Amputation,
he fumed, was out of the question. What use
is a son with one arm only? I would rather
he died. Let us go, he said, we are wasting
our time. I am sure the wrestler can do it.
If we must stay, there is the other hospital.

I argued and pleaded; it was no use.
There is no time, I said, the gangrene
is growing like a storm. But they would not listen.
I saw them go with a helpless rage
burning inside me. As I left the hospital
it was a lovely spring day, fresh after rain,
and I felt ashamed of being so healthy.
I heard the boy died on the operating table.

Taufiq Rafat

'Out, Out –'

The buzz saw snarled and rattled in the yard
And made dust and dropped stove-length sticks of wood,
Sweet-scented stuff when the breeze drew across it.
And from there those that lifted eyes could count
Five mountain ranges one behind the other
Under the sunset far into Vermont.
And the saw snarled and rattled, snarled and rattled,
As it ran light, or had to bear a load.
And nothing happened: day was all but done.
Call it a day, I wish they might have said
To please the boy by giving him the half hour
That a boy counts so much when saved from work.
His sister stood beside them in her apron
To tell them 'Supper'. At the word, the saw,
As if to prove saws knew what supper meant,
Leaped out at the boy's hand, or seemed to leap –
He must have given the hand. However it was,
Neither refused the meeting. But the hand!
The boy's first outcry was a rueful laugh,
As he swung toward them holding up the hand
Half in appeal, but half as if to keep
The life from spilling. Then the boy saw all –
Since he was old enough to know, big boy
Doing a man's work, though a child at heart –
He saw all spoiled. 'Don't let him cut my hand off –
The doctor, when he comes. Don't let him sister!'
So. But the hand was gone already.
The doctor put him in the dark of ether.
He lay and puffed his lips out with his breath.
And then – the watcher at his pulse took fright.
No one believed. They listened at his heart.
Little – less – nothing! – and that ended it.
No more to build on there. And they, since they
Were not the one dead, turned to their affairs.

Robert Frost

Part Two
Themes

My Kind of People

I try to think what someone you read about would be like to meet. What would they say? What would they do?

I like to see if I can find just four or five words that fit a person as perfectly as possible.

*W*aiting for Thelma's Laughter

(for Thelma, my West Indian born Afro-American neighbour)

You wanna take the world
in hand
and fix-it-up
the way you fix your living room

You wanna reach out and crush
life's big and small injustices
in the fire and honey
of your hands

You wanna scream
cause your head's too small
for your dreams

and the children
                running round
                    acting like lil clowns
                        breaking the furniture down

while I sit through
it all watching you
knowing any time now
your laughter's gonna come

to drown and heal us all

Grace Nichols

To a Crippled Schoolmaster

We hogged the billiard table in your room,
We read your weekly *Mirrors* with delight;
And if some little cretin went too far
Your magisterial wit would put him right.

I still recall your dragging up the stairs
And setting out some time before each bell;
I liked your funny classes (though in truth
I really cannot claim you taught us well).

We watched you crawl from bad to worse,
Drag slower and slower until the term
You didn't walk: your classes came
To see you fade from ailing to infirm.

When you retired from teaching, as you had to
– Your body wouldn't serve your driving will –
We built a special house to cage you in
So anyone could come and see you still.

The few occasions when I looked you up
I saw a living carcass wasting slow,
That sprightliness of mind a crudish irony
When all your wretched limbs were withering so.

Without a conscious plan to be neglectful
I didn't seem to find the time
To drop in for your running commentary
On what you called 'the national pantomime'.

I wonder whether time has stolen from me
Something that matters deeply (or should do)
And whether anything I manage now will ever
Relieve my guilt about neglecting you.

And when you die I know I shall be sorry,
Remembering your kindness. But the fear
Of facing death stops me from coming
To see you dying smiling in your chair.

Mervyn Morris

*G*reat Grandfather's Bridge

I stop. The rock-halted slope
is dense with sounds. Far off,
a train has left
Great-grandfather's bridge
on the long way south.
The illusion of his presence
knocks in my mind. I can see him
standing in that very place,
with the rush of water
coming at him as he thinks
the problem through. They had built

the bridge two seasons running,
and seen the monsoon flood
undermine it twice
to smash it down. Nothing worked.
The concrete pieces lay about downstream.
Then someone thought of him,
Great-grandfather, living out
the last of his life
in an unexceptional town.
They sent a man to ask him,
and he came – bringing only his

honest reputation as the very best
builder of bridges
in the central provinces.
But that had been years ago.
He could not have known
of subsequent techniques.
Would the gamble work?
He said nothing to allay their doubt,
explained nothing,
just got off at the railhead
and walked up and down the bank

of the fast stream, prodding
at the ground with his stick,
and stopped,
and stood there thinking.
The men who had sent for him
hovered anxiously.
They must have thought the old man mad.
But he knew bridges. Build here,
he said, making a sign,
then walked back to the station
to wait for his train. For months,

I was told three generations later,
the argument raged.
There were those who said
it was just as well
the old man had been pensioned.
And others who insisted
it would do no harm to try.
After all, it was only a small bridge
and hadn't cost very much the other times.
They could bear the loss
And if it worked, several promotions

were assured. So they went ahead
and built it exactly where
Great-grandfather had said
it should be.
From where I stand
I can see the clean, concrete arch,
thrust and tension matched,
etched precisely
against a monsoon sky.
A train whistles, and the flooded stream
races below the humming deck.

Kaleem Omar

My Uncle E.P.M. Harawa

Don't call it perfect timing
when my uncle emerges
from nowhere
leading a procession
of men, women and children
bearing groundnuts, potatoes
and fresh maize

With shoulders upright
and marching as to war
he has always been
the source of wonders among men –
always emerging from nowhere
to stand where we needed him
at the moment that we needed him –

What would Malawians
around the mining towns
of Selukwe, Shabani, Guinea Fowl
have done without him?

I see him now
in his white coat
stethoscope slung on his shoulders
muttering 'Oh yes'
through rows of patients
in the hospital at Camper Down

I see him again
Sundays this time
right in front of the congregation
and to this day up there in
Mbulunji, a tower of strength
to the Church of Central Africa, Presbyterian.

Will our children ever follow
the love that sends a man
at the break of day
to gather the choicest maize and the choicest fruit
and wait close to the roadside
to emerge quietly
as the van to Zomba
comes in view?

Don't call it perfect timing:
he has always been
where he was to be
at the minute he was to be
like his ancestor Kajimerere
who it is said
explained his origins by saying,
'I grew out of this land.'

Felix Mnthali

*P*oem at Thirty-Nine

How I miss my father.
I wish he had not been
so tired
when I was
born.

Writing deposit slips and checks
I think of him.
He taught me how.
This is the form,
he must have said:
the way it is done.
I learned to see
bits of paper
as a way
to escape
the life he knew
and even in high school
had a savings
account.

He taught me
that telling the truth
did not always mean
a beating;
though many of my truths
must have grieved him
before the end.

How I miss my father!
He cooked like a person
dancing
in a yoga meditation
and craved the voluptuous
sharing
of good food.

Now I look and cook just like him:
my brain light;
tossing this and that
into the pot;
seasoning none of my life
the same way twice; happy to feed
whoever strays my way.

He would have grown
to admire
the woman I've become:
cooking, writing, chopping wood,
staring into the fire.

Alice Walker

*F*or My Sister Molly Who in the Fifties

Once made a fairy rooster from
Mashed potatoes
Whose eyes I forget
But green onions were his tail
And his two legs were carrot sticks
A tomato slice his crown.
Who came home on vacation
When the sun was hot
and cooked
and cleaned
And minded least of all
The children's questions
A million or more
Pouring in on her
Who had been to school
And knew (and told us too) that certain
Words were no longer good
And taught me not to say us for we
No matter what 'Sonny said' up the road.

FOR MY SISTER MOLLY WHO IN THE FIFTIES
Knew Hamlet well and read into the night
And coached me in my songs of Africa
A continent I never knew
But learned to love
Because 'they' she said could carry
A tune
And spoke in accents never heard
In Eatonton.
Who read from *Prose and Poetry*
And loved to read 'Sam McGee from Tennessee'
On nights the fire was burning low
And Christmas wrapped in angel hair
And I for one prayed for snow.

WHO IN THE FIFTIES
Knew all the written things that made
Us laugh and stories by
The hour   Waking up the story buds

Like fruit. Who walked among the flowers
And brought them inside the house
And smelled as good as they
And looked as bright.
Who made dresses, braided
Hair. Moved chairs about
Hung things from walls
Ordered baths
Frowned on wasp bites
And seemed to know the endings
Of all the tales
I had forgot.

WHO OFF INTO THE UNIVERSITY
Went exploring   To London and
To Rotterdam
Prague and to Liberia
Bringing back the news to us
Who knew none of it
But followed
crops and weather
funerals and
Methodist Homecoming;
easter speeches,
groaning church.

WHO FOUND ANOTHER WORLD
Another life   With gentlefolk
Far less trusting
And moved and moved and changed
Her name
And sounded precise
When she spoke   And frowned away
Our sloppishness.

WHO SAW US SILENT
Cursed with fear   A love burning
Inexpressible
And sent me money not for me
But for 'College'.
Who saw me grow through letters
The words misspelled   But not

The longing   Stretching
Growth
The tied and twisting
Tongue
Feet no longer bare
Skin no longer burnt against
The cotton.

WHO BECAME SOMEONE OVERHEAD
A light   A thousand watts
Bright and also blinding
And saw my brothers cloddish
And me destined to be
Wayward
My mother remote   My father
A wearisome farmer
With heartbreaking
Nails.

FOR MY SISTER MOLLY WHO IN THE FIFTIES
Found much
Unbearable
Who walked where few had
Understood   And sensed our
Groping after light
And saw some extinguished
And no doubt mourned.

FOR MY SISTER MOLLY WHO IN THE FIFTIES
Left us.

Alice Walker

Able

You don't take any notice of what you can do until you find you are unable to do it. It's not until something is taken away from you that you realize how valuable it is.

When you're disabled you don't want an opportunity to get some sympathy, you need an opportunity to get on with your life.

Does It Matter?

Does it matter – losing your legs? . . .
For people will always be kind,
And you need not show that you mind
When the others come in after hunting
To gobble their muffins and eggs.

Does it matter – losing your sight? . . .
There's such splendid work for the blind;
And people will always be kind,
As you sit on the terrace remembering
And turning your face to the light.

Do they matter – those dreams from the pit? . . .
You can drink and forget and be glad,
And people won't say that you're mad;
For they'll know that you've fought for your country,
And no one will worry a bit.

Siegfried Sassoon

In the Children's Hospital

'Does it matter? Losing your legs?'
SIEGFRIED SASSOON

Now let the legless boy show the great lady
How well he can manage his crutches.
It doesn't matter though the Sister objects,
'He's not used to them yet,' when such is
The will of the Princess. Come, Tommy,
Try a few desperate steps through the ward.
Then the hand of Royalty will pat your head
And life suddenly cease to be hard.
For a couple of legs are surely no miss
When the loss leads to such an honour as this!
One knows, when one sees how jealous the rest
Of the children are, it's been all for the best!–
But would the sound of your sticks on the floor
Thundered in her skull for evermore!

Hugh MacDiarmid

The Veteran

May, 1916

We came upon him sitting in the sun,
  Blinded by war, and left. And past the fence
There came young soldiers from the Hand and Flower,
  Asking advice of his experience.

And he said this, and that, and told them tales,
  And all the nightmares of each empty head
Blew into air; then, hearing us beside,
  'Poor chaps, how'd they know what it's like?' he said.

And we stood there, and watched him as he sat,
  Turning his sockets where they went away,
Until it came to one of us to ask
  'And you're – how old?'
'Nineteen, the third of May.'

Margaret Postgate Cole

Uncle Bert

My one-armed uncle Bert
Married a girl from Aberaman
And rented a tiny cottage in a dingle
At the end of a cart-track
Above the village of Brockweir.
There he toiled, earned a living
And raised six children.

He made fences, gates and cots,
Tended a kitchen garden,
Learnt all about animals
And became a countryman.
He did all this with a sleeve
Half empty and a right arm
As strong as a stout oak-branch.

In his youth he played the violin
With skill and lived at Gilfach.
At eighteen he was at Dardanelles
To maintain England's Glory.
But he never reached land
For as he waded in the sea
A Turk shot off half his arm.

For two years his violin
Hung above his soldier photograph.
My grandmother, his mother, told me
That on his return, his sleeve
Pinned to his shoulder,
He took down his instrument
And smashed it on the garden wall.

Robert Morgan

Broken Moon

for Emma

Twelve, small as six,
strength, movement, hearing
all given in half measure,
my daughter,
child of genetic carelessness,
walks uphill, always.

I watch her morning face;
precocious patience as she hooks each sock,
creeps it up her foot,
aims her jersey like a quoit.
My fingers twitch;
her private frown deters.

Her jokes can sting:
'My life is like dressed crab
– lot of effort, rather little meat.'
Yet she delights in seedlings taking root,
finding a fossil,
a surprise dessert.

Chopin will not yield to her stiff touch;
I hear her cursing.
She paces Bach exactly,
firm rounding of perfect cadences.
Somewhere inside
she is dancing a courante.

In dreams she skims the sand,
curls toes into the ooze of pools,
leaps on to stanchions.
Awake, her cousins take her hands;
they lean into the waves,
stick-child between curved sturdiness.

She turns away from stares,
laughs at the boy who asks
if she will find a midget husband.
Ten years ago, cradling her,
I showed her the slice of silver in the sky.
'Moon broken,' she said.

Carole Satyamurti

The Fifth Sense

A 65-year-old Cypriot Greek shepherd, Nicolis Loizou, was wounded by
security forces early today. He was challenged twice; when he failed to
answer, troops opened fire. A subsequent hospital examination showed that
the man was deaf.
News Item, 30 December 1957.

Lamps burn all the night
Here, where people must be watched and seen,
And I, a shepherd, Nicolis Loizou,
Wish for the dark, for I have been
Sure-footed in the dark, but now my sight
Stumbles among these beds, scattered white boulders,
As I lean towards my far slumbering house
With the night lying upon my shoulders.

My sight was always good,
Better than others. I could taste wine and bread
And name the field they spattered when the harvest
Broke. I could coil in the red
Scent of the fox out of a maze of wood
And grass. I could touch mist, I could touch breath.
But of my sharp senses I had only four.
The fifth one pinned me to my death.

The soldiers must have called
The word they needed: Halt. Not hearing it,
I was their failure, relaxed against the winter
Sky, the flag of their defeat.
With their five senses they could not have told
That I lacked one, and so they had to shoot.
They would fire at a rainbow if it had
A colour less than they were taught.

Patricia Beer

Creatures

If human beings were forced to be ordinary animals for a day or two, it would change the way they treated creatures.

I know what I think about animals but I often wonder what they think about me.

Animals

I think I could turn and live with animals, they are so placid
    and self-contained;
I stand and look at them long and long.

They do not sweat and whine about their condition;
They do not lie awake in the dark and weep for their sins;

They do not make me sick discussing their duty to God;
Not one is dissatisfied – not one is demented with the mania of
    owning things;

Not one kneels to another, nor to his kind that lived thousands
    of years ago;
Not one is respectable or industrious over the whole earth.

Walt Whitman

Elephant

It is quite unfair to be
obliged to be so large, so I suppose
you could call me discontented.

Think big, they said, when
I was a little elephant; they
wanted to get me used to it.

It was kind. But it doesn't help if,
inside, you are carefree in small ways,
fond of little amusements.

You are smaller than me, think
how conveniently near the flowers are,
how you can pat the cat by just

halfbending over. You can also
arrange teacups for dolls, play
marbles in the proper season.

I would give anything to be
able to do a tiny, airy, flitting
dance to show how very little a

thing happiness can be really.

Alan Brownjohn

A Bird Came Down the Walk

A Bird came down the Walk –
He did not know I saw –
He bit an Angleworm in halves
And ate the fellow, raw,

And then he drank a Dew
From a convenient Grass –
And then hopped sidewise to the Wall
To let a Beetle pass –

He glanced with rapid eyes
That hurried all around –
They looked like frightened Beads, I thought –
He stirred his Velvet Head

Like one in danger, Cautious,
I offered him a Crumb
And he unrolled his feathers
And rowed him softer home –

Than Oars divide the Ocean,
Too silver for a seam –
Or Butterflies, off Banks of Noon
Leap, plashless as they swim.

Emily Dickinson

*O*ne Gone, Eight to Go

On a night of savage frost,
This year, my smallest cat,
The fluffy one, got lost.
And I thought that that was that.

Until late home, I heard,
As I fumbled for my key,
The weak sound of some bird.
He was there, mewing to me.

There, on the icy sill,
Lifting his crusted head,
He looked far worse than ill.
He looked, I'd say, quite dead.

Indoors, though, he could eat,
And he showed, and fluffed his tail.
So much for a plate of meat.
So much for a storm of hail.

Now, by the burning grate,
I stroke his fragile spine,
Thinking of time, and fate.
Lives go. Men don't have nine,

As kittens do, to waste.
This lucky one survives,
And purrs, affronted-faced.
But even he, who thrives

Tonight, in my cupped hands,
And will grow big and grey,
Will sense, in time, the sands,
And fail, and shrink away.

George Macbeth

Kittens

There are too many kittens.
Even the cat is dismayed
at this overestimation
of her stock and slinks away.
Kind friends cannot adopt them all.

My relatives say: Take them
to a bazaar and let them go
each to his destiny. They'll live
off pickings. But they are so small
somebody may step on one
like a tomato.

Or too fastidious to soil
a polished shoe will kick it
out of his path. If they survive
the gaunt dogs and battering heels,
they will starve gently, squealing
a little less each day.

The European thing to do
is drown them. Warm water
is advised to lessen the shock.
They are so small it takes only
a minute. You hold them down
and turn your head away.

Then the water shatters. Your hands
are frantic eels. Oddly
like landed fish, their blunt pink mouths
open and shut. Legs strike out.
Each claw, a delicate nail
paring, is bared.

They are blind and will never know
you did this to them. The water
recomposes itself.
                    Snagged
by two cultures, which
shall I choose?

Maki Kureishi

Death of a Naturalist

All year the flax-dam festered in the heart
Of the townland; green and heavy headed
Flax had rotted there, weighted down by huge sods.
Daily it sweltered in the punishing sun.
Bubbles gargled delicately, bluebottles
Wove a strong gauze of sound around the smell.
There were dragon-flies, spotted butterflies,
But best of all was the warm thick slobber
Of frogspawn that grew like clotted water
In the shade of the banks. Here, every spring
I would fill jampotfuls of the jellied
Specks to range on window-sills at home,
On shelves at school, and wait and watch until
The fattening dots burst into nimble-
Swimming tadpoles. Miss Walls would tell us how
The daddy frog was called a bullfrog
And how he croaked and how the mammy frog
Laid hundreds of little eggs and this was
Frogspawn. You could tell the weather by frogs too
For they were yellow in the sun and brown
In rain.

       Then one hot day when fields were rank
With cowdung in the grass the angry frogs
Invaded the flax-dam; I ducked through hedges
To a coarse croaking that I had not heard
Before. The air was thick with a bass chorus.
Right down the dam gross-bellied frogs were cocked
On sods; their loose necks pulsed like sails. Some hopped:
The slap and plop were obscene threats. Some sat
Poised like mud grenades, their blunt heads farting.
I sickened, turned, and ran. The great slime kings
Were gathered there for vengeance and I knew
That if I dipped my hand the spawn would clutch it.

Seamus Heaney

*S*tory

Ballads are like television serials: you keep on reading to find out what happens next.

What interests me about most ballads is that you only get one side of the story.

The Death of Ben Hall

Ben Hall was out on the Lachlan side
With a thousand pounds on his head;
A score of troopers were scattered wide
And a hundred more were ready to ride
Wherever a rumour led.

They had followed his track from the Weddin heights
And north by the Weelong yards;
Through dazzling days and moonlit nights
They had sought him over their rifle-sights,
With their hands on their trigger-guards.

The outlaw stole like a hunted fox
Through the scrub and stunted heath,
And peered like a hawk from his eyrie rocks
Through the waving boughs of the sapling box
On the troopers riding beneath.

His clothes were rent by the clutching thorn
And his blistered feet were bare;
Ragged and torn, with his beard unshorn,
He hid in the woods like a beast forlorn,
With a padded path to this lair.

But every night when the white stars rose
He crossed by the Gunning Plain
To a stockman's hut where the Gunning flows,
And struck on the door three swift light blows,
And a hand unhooked the chain –

And the outlaw followed the line path back
With food for another day;
And the kindly darkness covered his track
And the shadows swallowed him deep and black
Where the starlight melted away.

But his friend had read of the Big Reward,
And his soul was stirred with greed;
He fastened his horse and crossed the ford,
And spurred to the town at speed.

A hot wind blew from the Lachlan bank
And a curse on its shoulder came;
The pine-trees frowned at him, rank on rank,
The sun on a gathering storm-cloud sank
And flushed his cheek with shame.

He reined at the Court; and the tale began
That the rifles alone should end;
Sergeant and trooper laid their plan
To draw the net on a hunted man
At the treacherous word of a friend.

False was the hand that raised the chain
And false was the whispered word:
'The troopers have turned to the south again,
You may dare to camp on the Gunning Plain,'
And the weary outlaw heard.

He walked from the hut but a quarter-mile
Where a clump of saplings stood
In a sea of grass like a lonely isle;
And the moon came up in a little while
Like silver steeped in blood.

Ben Hall lay down on the dew-wet ground
By the side of his tiny fire.
And a night-breeze woke, and he heard no sound
As the troopers drew their cordon round –
And the traitor earned his hire.

And nothing they saw in the dim grey light,
But the little glow in the trees;
And they crouched in the tall cold grass all night,
Each one ready to shoot at sight,
With his rifle cocked on his knees.

When the shadows broke and the dawn's white sword
Swung over the mountain wall,
And a little wind blew over the ford,
A sergeant sprang to his feet and roared:
'In the name of the Queen, Ben Hall!'

Haggard, the outlaw leapt from his bed
With his lean arms held on high.
'Fire!' And the word was scarcely said
When the mountains rang to a rain of lead –
And the dawn went drifting by.

They kept their word and they paid his pay
Where a clean man's hand would shrink;
And that was the traitor's master-day
As he stood by the bar on his homeward way
And called on the crowd to drink.

He banned no creed and he barred no class,
And he called to his friends by name;
But the worst would shake his head and pass
And none would drink from the bloodstained glass
And the goblet red with shame.

Anon

64

The Ballad of Charlotte Dymond

Charlotte Dymond, a domestic servant aged eighteen, was murdered near Rowtor Ford on Bodmin Moor on Sunday 14 April 1844 by her young man: a crippled farm-hand, Matthew Weeks, aged twenty-two. A stone marks the spot.

It was a Sunday evening
  And in the April rain
That Charlotte went from our house
  And never came home again.

Her shawl of diamond redcloth,
  She wore a yellow gown,
She carried the green gauze handkerchief
  She bought in Bodmin town.

About her throat her necklace
  And in her purse her pay:
The four silver shillings
  She had at Lady Day.

In her purse four shillings
  And in her purse her pride
As she walked out one evening
  Her lover at her side.

Out beyond the marshes
  Where the cattle stand,
With her crippled lover
  Limping at her hand.

Charlotte walked with Matthew
  Through the Sunday mist,
Never saw the razor
  Waiting at his wrist.

Charlotte she was gentle
  But they found her in the flood
Her Sunday beads among the reeds
  Beaming with her blood.

Matthew, where is Charlotte,
  And wherefore has she flown?
For you walked out together
  And now are come alone.

Why do you not answer,
  Stand silent as a tree,
Your Sunday worsted stockings
  All muddied to the knee?

Why do you mend your breast-pleat
  With a rusty needle's thread
And fall with fears and silent tears
  Upon your single bed?

Why do you sit so sadly
  Your face the colour of clay
And with a green gauze handkerchief
  Wipe the sour sweat away?

Has she gone to Blisland
  To seek an easier place,
And is that why your eye won't dry
  And blinds your bleaching face?

'Take me home!' cried Charlotte,
  'I lie here in the pit!
A red rock rests upon my breasts
  And my naked neck is split!'

Her skin was soft as sable,
  Her eyes were wide as day,
Her hair was blacker than the bog
  That licked her life away.

Her cheeks were made of honey,
  Her throat was made of flame
Where all around the razor
  Had written its red name.

As Matthew turned at Plymouth
  About the tilting Hoe,
The cold and cunning constable
  Up to him did go:

'I've come to take you, Matthew,
   Unto the magistrate's door.
Come quiet now, you pretty poor boy,
   And you must know what for.'

'She is as pure,' cried Matthew,
   'As is the early dew,
Her only stain it is the pain
   That round her neck I drew!

'She is as guiltless as the day
   She sprang forth from her mother.
The only sin upon her skin
   Is that she loved another.'

They took him off to Bodmin,
   They pulled the prison bell,
They sent him smartly up to heaven
   And dropped him down to hell.

All through the granite kingdom
   And on its travelling airs
Ask which of these two lovers
   The most deserves your prayers.

And your steel heart search, Stranger,
   That you may pause and pray
For lovers who come not to bed
   Upon their wedding day,

But lie upon the moorland
   Where stands the sacred snow
Above the breathing river,
   And the salt sea-winds go.

Charles Causley

The Daemon Lover

'O where hae you been, my long, long love,
  This long seven years and more?'
'O I'm come to seek my former vows
  That ye promised me before.'

'O hold your tongue of your former vows,
  For they will breed sad strife;
O hold your tongue of your former vows
  For I am become a wife.'

He turned him right and round about,
  And the tear blinded his ee*:   * _eye_
'I would never hae trodden on Irish ground,
  If it had not been for thee.

'I might hae had a king's daughter,
  Far, far beyond the sea;
I might have had a king's daughter,
  Had it not been for love o' thee.'

'If ye might have had a king's daughter,
  Yeself ye had to blame;
Ye might have taken the king's daughter,
  For ye kend* that I was nane.†   * _knew_ † _none_

'If I was to leave my husband dear,
  And my two babes also,
O what have you to take me to,
  If with you I should go?'

'I have seven ships upon the sea –
  And the eighth brought me to land –
With four-and-twenty bold mariners,
  And music on every hand.'

She has taken up her two little babes,
  Kissed them both cheek and chin:
'O fare ye well, my own two babes,
  For I'll never see you again.'

She set her foot upon the ship,
  No mariners could she behold;
But the sails were made of taffeta,
  And the masts of beaten gold.

She had not sailed a league, a league,
  A league but barely three,
Till grim, grim grew his countenance,
  And gurly* grew his ee.   * *stormy*

They had not sailed a league, a league,
  A league but barely three,
Until she espied his cloven foot,
  And she wept right bitterly.

'O hold your tongue of your weeping,' says he,
  'Of your weeping now let me be;
I will shew you how the lilies grow
  On the banks of Italy.'

'O what hills are yon, yon pleasant hills,
  That the sun shines sweetly on?'
'O yon are the hills of heaven,' he said,
  'Where you will never win.'

'O whaten* a mountain is yon,' she said,   *what kind of*
  'All so dreary with frost and snow?'
'O yon is the mountain of hell,' he cried,
  'Where you and I will go.'

He struck the top-mast with his hand,
  The fore-mast with his knee,
And he broke that gallant ship in twain,
  And sank her in the sea.

Anon

Mary Cummings

They heard her singing in her prison
   Dressed in bridal white;
They heard the ringing of the deathbell
   As the sun slid into sight.

They asked for her forgiveness
   For what they had to do;
They offered her a prayer-book
   And a rosary too.

Mary Cummings woke one spring morning
   To dress in her best gown,
To bless the man she was to wed
   That spring morning in town.

Mary Cummings blessed the birds that sang,
   The sun that glittered down;
She blessed her lord with all her heart
   And she blessed her bridal gown.

She rode towards the ancient kirk
   With two maids at her side
And the folk who watched her waved to her,
   Warmed to a beautiful bride.

She stopped outside the ancient kirk
   And smiled as she stepped inside
Looking for the man who'd claimed
   Mary Cummings for his bride.

She saw her lover's father,
   She watched him turn aside;
She saw her lover's mother
   But no groom for a bride.

Mary Cummings cursed that father,
   She wished that old man blind
So that sad old man would never see
   The pain in Mary's mind.

Mary Cummings cursed that mother,
    For bearing such a child
Who could leave Mary Cummings in her bridal gown
    Abandoned and defiled.

The mother slithered to the ground,
    The father's eyes went white;
Mary called on hell to hound their son
    And to claim his soul that night.

She cursed at their forgiveness,
    She praised what they had to do;
She threw aside their prayer-book
    And their rosary too.

She kept on singing in her prison
    As the sun slid out of sight
And prepared for her dark new lover
    In her bridal gown of white.

Alan Bold

*L*ove More or Less

It's the poems about falling out of love that make more sense to me.

Love is the one thing that never changes. People who wrote centuries ago seem to have felt the same as I do. It's only the way you use words that alters a little.

He Wishes for the Cloths of Heaven

Had I the heavens' embroidered cloths,
Enwrought with golden and silver light,
The blue and the dim and the dark cloths
Of night and light and the half-light,
I would spread the cloths under your feet:
But I, being poor, have only my dreams;
I have spread my dreams under your feet;
Tread softly because you tread on my dreams.

W. B. Yeats

To Women, as Far as I'm Concerned

The feelings I don't have I don't have.
The feelings I don't have, I won't say I have.
The feelings you say you have, you don't have.
The feelings you would like us both to have, we neither of us
   have.
The feelings people ought to have, they never have.
If people say they've got feelings, you may be pretty sure they
   haven't got them.
So if you want either of us to feel anything at all
you'd better abandon all idea of feelings altogether.

D.H. Lawrence

First Love

I ne'er was struck before that hour
   With love so sudden and so sweet
Her face it bloomed like a sweet flower
   And stole my heart away complete
My face turned pale a deadly pale
   My legs refused to walk away
And when she looked what could I ail
My life and all seemed turned to clay

And then my blood rushed to my face
   And took my eyesight quite away
The trees and bushes round the place
   Seemed midnight at noon day
I could not see a single thing
   Words from my eyes did start
They spoke as chords do from the string
   And blood burnt round my heart

Are flowers the winters choice
   Is love's bed always snow
She seemed to hear my silent voice
   Not loves appeals to know
I never saw so sweet a face
   As that I stood before
My heart has left its dwelling place
   And can return no more –

John Clare

The Tigers of Pain

The tigers of pain
Prowl out in the rain
Not far from the circle of light
Behind our locked doors
Their passionate roars
Assault us by day and by night

The famines and wars
On faraway shores
Send echoes that batter your heart
There's fire and flood
And spilling of blood
You wait for your troubles to start

When love comes along
Your head's full of song
It's hard to stay sober and sane
But be on your guard
For out in the yard
Are the terrible tigers of pain

Fran Landesman

Let Me Not to the Marriage of True Minds

Let me not to the marriage of true minds
Admit impediments: love is not love
Which alters when it alteration finds,
Or bends with the remover to remove.
O, no, it is an ever-fixed mark
That looks on tempests and is never shaken;
It is the star to every wand'ring bark,
Whose worth's unknown, although his height be taken.
Love's not Time's fool, though rosy lips and cheeks
Within his bending sickle's compass come;
Love alters not with his brief hours and weeks,
But bears it out even to the edge of doom.
   If this be error and upon me proved,
   I never writ, nor no man ever loved.

William Shakespeare

Envy

He was the first always: Fortune
   Shone bright in his face.
I fought for years; with no effort
   He conquered the place:
We ran; my feet were all bleeding,
   But he won the race.

Spite of his many successes
   Men loved him the same;
My one pale ray of good fortune
   Met scoffing and blame.
When we erred, they gave him pity,
   But me – only shame.

My home was still in the shadow,
   His lay in the sun:
I longed in vain: what he asked for
   It straightway was done.
Once I staked all my heart's treasure,
   We played – and he won.

Yes; and just now I have seen him,
   Cold, smiling, and blest,
Laid in his coffin. God help me!
   While he is at rest,
I am cursed still to live: – even
   Death loved him the best.

Adelaide Anne Procter

The Smile

There is a Smile of Love,
And there is a Smile of Deceit,
And there is a Smile of Smiles
In which these two Smiles meet.

And there is a Frown of Hate,
And there is a Frown of disdain,
And there is a Frown of Frowns
Which you strive to forget in vain,

For it sticks in the Heart's deep Core
And it sticks in the deep Back bone;
And no Smile that ever was smil'd,
But only one Smile alone,

That betwixt the Cradle & Grave
It only once Smil'd can be;
But, when it once is Smil'd,
There's an end to all Misery.

William Blake

The Lie

Today, you threaten to leave me.
I hold curses, in my mouth,
which could flood your path, sear
bottomless chasms in your road.

I keep, behind my lips,
invectives capable of tearing
the septum from your
nostrils and the skin from your back.

Tears, copious as a spring rain,
are checked in ducts
and screams are crowded in a corner
of my throat.

You are leaving?

Aloud, I say:
I'll help you pack, but it's getting late,
I have to hurry or miss my date.
When I return, I know you'll be gone.
Do drop a line or telephone.

Maya Angelou

The Parting

Since there's no help, come let us kiss and part –
Nay, I have done, you get no more of me;
And I am glad, yea, glad with all my heart,
That thus so cleanly I myself can free.
Shake hands for ever, cancel all our vows,
And when we meet at any time again,
Be it not seen in either of our brows
That we one jot of former love retain.
Now at the last gasp of Love's latest breath,
When, his pulse failing, Passion speechless lies,
When Faith is kneeling by his bed of death,
And Innocence is closing up his eyes,
   –Now if thou wouldst, when all have given him over,
   From death to life thou might'st him yet recover.

Michael Drayton

Remember

Remember me when I am gone away,
   Gone far away into the silent land;
   When you can no more hold me by the hand,
Nor I half turn to go yet turning stay.
Remember me when no more day by day
   You tell me of our future that you planned:
   Only remember me; you understand
It will be late to counsel then or pray.
Yet if you should forget me for a while
   And afterwards remember, do not grieve:
   For if the darkness and corruption leave
   A vestige of the thoughts that once I had,
Better by far you should forget and smile
   Than that you should remember and be sad.

Christina Rossetti

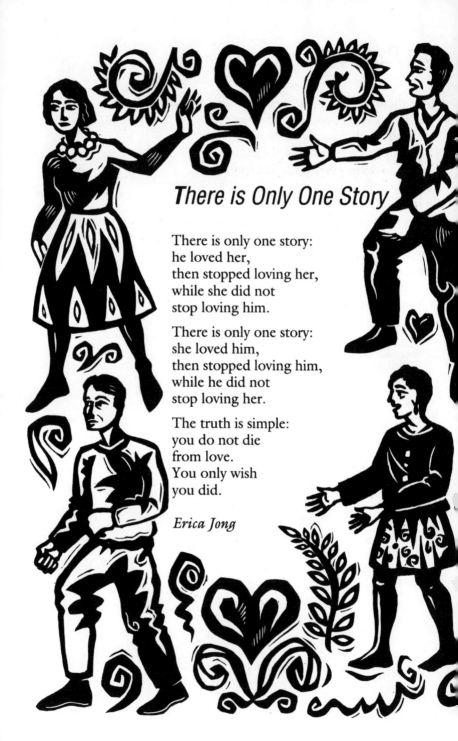

There is Only One Story

There is only one story:
he loved her,
then stopped loving her,
while she did not
stop loving him.

There is only one story:
she loved him,
then stopped loving him,
while he did not
stop loving her.

The truth is simple:
you do not die
from love.
You only wish
you did.

Erica Jong

Not So Serious

People say they don't like poetry but everyone enjoys a laugh, so everyone enjoys a poem if it makes them laugh.

Some humorous poetry makes me laugh because it is just plain silly. Other poems amuse me because they remind me of something that has happened.

*B*ritish Rail Regrets

British Rail regrets
having to regret.
British Rail regrets
it cannot spell.
British Rail regrets
the chalk ran out.
British Rail regrets
that due to a staff shortage
there will be no one
to offer regrets.
British Rail regrets,
but will not be sending
flowers or tributes.
British Rail regrets
the early arrival
of your train.
This was due to industrious action.
British Rail regrets
that because of a work-to-rule
by our tape machine
this is a real person.
British Rail regrets
the cheese shortage
in your sandwich.
This is due to
a points failure.
The steward got
three out of ten.

British Rail regrets.
Tears flow from beneath
the locked doors of staff rooms.
Red-eyed ticket collectors
offer comfort
to stranded passengers.
Angry drivers threaten
to come out in sympathy
with the public.

British Rail regrets.
That's why its members
are permanently dressed in black.
That's why porters stand around
as if in a state of shock.
That's why Passenger Information
is off the hook.

British Rail regrets
that due to the shortage of regrets
there will be a train.

Steve Turner

Mary's Ghost

'Twas in the middle of the night,
    To sleep young William tried,
When Mary's ghost came stealing in,
    And stood at his bedside.

O William dear! O William dear!
    My rest eternal ceases;
Alas! my everlasting peace
    Is broken into pieces!

I thought the last of all my cares
    Would end with my last minute;
But, though I went to my long home,
    I didn't stay long in it.

The body-snatchers they have come,
    And made a snatch at me;
It's very hard them kind of men
    Won't let a body be.

You thought that I was buried deep,
    Quite decent like and chary,
But from her grave in Mary-Bone
    They've come and boned your Mary.

The arm that used to take your arm
    Is took to Dr Vyse;
And both my legs are gone to walk
    The hospital at Guy's.

I vowed that you should have my hand,
    But fate gives us denial;
You'll find it there, at Dr Bell's
    In spirits and a phial.

As for my feet, the little feet,
    You used to call so pretty,
There's one, I know, in Bedford Row,
    The t'other's in the City.

I can't tell where my head is gone,
    But Dr Carpune can;
As for my trunk, it's all packed up
    To go by Pickford's van.

I wish you'd go to Mr P
    And save me such a ride;
I don't half like the outside place
    They've took for my inside.

The cock it crows – I must be gone!
    My William, we must part!
But I'll be yours in death, although
    Sir Astley has my heart.

Don't go to weep upon my grave
    And think that there I be:
They haven't left an atom there
    Of my anatomy.

Thomas Hood

The Horse That Had a Flat Tire

Once upon a valley
there came down
from some goldenblue mountains
a handsome young prince
who was riding
a dawncolored horse
named Lordsburg.

> I love you
> You're my breathing castle
> Gentle so gentle
> We'll live forever

In the valley
there was a beautiful maiden
whom the prince
drifted into love with
like a New Mexico made from
apple thunder and long
glass beads.

> I love you
> You're my breathing castle
> Gentle so gentle
> We'll live forever

The prince enchanted
the maiden
and they rode off
on the dawncolored horse
named Lordsburg
toward the goldenblue mountains.

> I love you
> You're my breathing castle
> Gentle so gentle
> We'll live forever

They would have lived
happily ever after
if the horse hadn't had
a flat tire
in front of a dragon's
house.

Richard Brautigan

*C*old Head, Cold Heart

I suppose no one has ever died of a head cold
while not fearing or fervently
wishing to do so on the hour,
gasping through a nose the size of Detroit.

My mouth tastes of moldy sneaker.
My tongue is big as a liverwurst.
My throat steams like a sewer.
The gnome of snot has stuck a bicycle pump in my ear.

I am a quagmire, a slithy bog.
I exude effluvia, mumbled curses,
and a dropsy of wads of paper,
handkerchiefs like little leprosies.

The world is an irritant
full of friends jumping in noisy frolic.
The damned healthy: I breathe on them.
My germs are my only comfort.

Marge Piercy

Prejudiced

With one person it's their size, with another it's their colour. Prejudice is the same whatever people pick on. And it hurts more than anyone admits.

Prejudice is so silly. Everyone is an individual so why can't people enjoy the differences?

The Colour of His Hair

Oh who is that young sinner with the handcuffs on his wrists?
And what has he been after that they groan and shake their fists?
And wherefore is he wearing such a conscience-stricken air?
Oh they're taking him to prison for the colour of his hair.

'Tis a shame to human nature, such a head of hair as his;
In the good old time 'twas hanging for the colour that it is;
Though hanging isn't bad enough and flaying would be fair
For the nameless and abominable colour of his hair.

Oh a deal of pains he's taken and a pretty price he's paid
To hide his poll or dye it of a mentionable shade;
But they've pulled the beggar's hat off for the world to see and
  stare,
And they're haling him to justice for the colour of his hair.

Now 'tis oakum for his fingers and the treadmill for his feet
And the quarry-gang on Portland in the cold and in the heat,
And between his spells of labour in the time he has to spare
He can curse the God that made him for the colour of his hair.

A.E. Houseman

Indian Children Speak

People said, 'Indian children are hard to teach.
Don't expect them to talk.'
One day stubby little Boy said,
'Last night the moon went all the way with me,
When I went out to walk.'
People said, 'Indian children are very silent.
Their only words are no and yes.'
But, ragged Pansy confided softly,
'My dress is old, but at night the moon is kind;
Then I wear a beautiful moon-colored dress.'
People said, 'Indian children are dumb.
They seldom make a reply.'
Clearly I hear Delores answer,
'Yes, the sunset is so good, I think God is throwing
A bright shawl around the shoulders of the sky.'
People said, 'Indian children have no affection.
They just don't care for anyone.'
Then I feel Ramon's hand and hear him whisper,
'A wild animal races in me since my mother sleeps
under the ground. Will it always run and run?'
People said, 'Indian children are rude.
They don't seem very bright.'
Then I remember Joe Henry's remark,
'The tree is hanging down her head because the sun
is staring at her. White people always stare.
They do not know it is not polite.'
People said, 'Indian children never take you in,
Outside their thoughts you'll always stand.'
I have forgotten the idle words that People said,
But treasure the day when iron doors swung wide,
And I slipped into the heart of Indian Land.

Juanita Bell

Erdywurble

My father's parents sold fish.
At school, Greek scholars taunted him,
the scholarship boy,
called him 'bromos', said he stank of fish.
His gifts withered; he learned
a stammer that stayed with him for life,
words jumping like the tiddlers he tried to catch
in the canal.

But from the fractured syllables, there grew
words of his own: 'Don't arrap',
he'd say when we were plaguing him.
'Pass me the erdywurble' – we in giggles
guessing what it was. 'I'm mogadored'
when the last crossword clue eluded him.
'It won't ackle', trying to splint
a broken geranium.

Unable to persuade the doctor
to help him die while he still knew himself,
his words trickled, stopped. Keening continually,
he stumbled on, mistaking night for day,
my mother for his own,
then recognizing no one. Just once,
answering his new granddaughter's cry, he said
'poor kippet'.

Carole Satyamurti

Mysteries

Sometimes a poem that is supposed to be mysterious leaves me feeling cheated. I want to know more and I never will.

I like poems that leave something to the imagination: where you can have your own ideas about who the person was or what has happened.

The Song of Wandering Aengus

I went out to the hazel wood,
Because a fire was in my head,
And cut and peeled a hazel wand,
And hooked a berry to a thread;
And when white moths were on the wing,
And moth-like stars were flickering out,
I dropped the berry in a stream
And caught a little silver trout.

When I had laid it on the floor
I went to blow the fire aflame,
But something rustled on the floor,
And some one called me by my name:
It had become a glimmering girl
With apple blossom in her hair
Who called me by my name and ran
And faded through the brightening air.

Though I am old with wandering
Through hollow lands and hilly lands,
I will find out where she has gone,
And kiss her lips and take her hands;
And walk among long dappled grass,
And pluck till time and times are done
The silver apples of the moon,
The golden apples of the sun.

W. B. Yeats

A Dream of Snow

I woke to find our room
was open to the stars.
During that night the snow had come,
drifting through spaces where rafters

should have been. (The tiles had slid
off silently to shatter on the ground.)
Familiar things were hid:
I knew my slippers by the mound

of snowflakes there;
the mirror by its struggle to reflect
untrod carpet and frosted chair.
The clock I could detect

by a regular, muffled tick.
'Quilted' I knew, was inadequate.
And though the snow lay thick
we were neither cold nor wet.

I tried to wake you then
to tell of what I'd seen
but was unable. When
I spoke words were frozen

into crystals on the quiet air.
I'd left the wardrobe open: in a queue behind the door
the stiffened shapes of our former
lives were waiting for the thaw.

Ian Parks

The Tide Rises, the Tide Falls

The tide rises, the tide falls,
The twilight darkens, the curlew calls;
Along the sea-sands damp and brown
The traveller hastens toward the town,
    And the tide rises, the tide falls.

Darkness settles on roofs and walls,
But the sea, the sea in the darkness calls;
The little waves, with their soft, white hands,
Efface the footprints in the sands,
    And the tide rises, the tide falls.

The morning breaks; the steeds in their stalls
Stamp and neigh, as the hostler calls;
The day returns, but nevermore
Returns the traveller to the shore,
    And the tide rises, the tide falls.

H. W. Longfellow

*O*zymandias

I met a traveller from an antique land
Who said: Two vast and trunkless legs of stone
Stand in the desert . . . Near them, on the sand,
Half sunk, a shattered visage lies, whose frown,
And wrinkled lip, and sneer of cold command,
Tell that its sculptor well those passions read
Which yet survive, stamped on these lifeless things,
The hand that mocked them, and the heart that fed:
And on the pedestal these words appear:
'My name is Ozymandias, king of kings:
Look on my works, ye Mighty, and despair!'
Nothing beside remains. Round the decay
Of that colossal wreck, boundless and bare
The lone and level sands stretch far away.

Percy Bysshe Shelley

Moments in Time

Poets very rarely tell you why they chose to describe a particular moment. You have to guess why it was important to them.

Some incidents seem very unimportant in themselves but they can remind you of all sorts of other things. The incident is a sort of opening door.

Incident

When you were lying on the white sand,
A rock under your head, and smiling,
(Circled by dead shells), I came to you
And you said, reaching to take my hand,
'Lie down'. So for a time we lay
Warm on the sand, talking and smoking,
Easy; while the grovelling sea behind
Sucked at the rocks and measured the day.
Lightly I fell asleep then, and fell
Into a cavernous dream of falling.
It was all the cave-myths, it was all
The myths of tunnel or tower or well –
Alice's rabbit-hole into the ground,
Or the path of Orpheus: a spiral staircase
To hell, furnished with danger and doubt.
Stumbling, I suddenly woke; and found
Water about me. My hair was wet,
And you were sitting on the grey sand,
Waiting for the lapping tide to take me:
Watching, and lighting a cigarette.

Fleur Adcock

Manwatching

From across the party I watch you,
Watching her.
Do my possessive eyes
Imagine your silent messages?
I think not.
She looks across at you
And telegraphs her flirtatious reply.
I have come to recognize this code,
You are on intimate terms with this pretty stranger,
And there is nothing I can do,
My face is calm, expressionless,
But my eyes burn into your back.
While my insides shout with rage.
She weaves her way towards you,
Turning on a bewitching smile.
I can't see your face, but you are mesmerised I expect.
I can predict you: I know this scene so well,
Some acquaintance grabs your arm,
You turn and meet my accusing stare head on,
Her eyes follow yours, meet mine,
And then slide away, she understands,
She's not interested enough to compete.
It's over now.
She fades away, you drift towards me,
'I'm bored' you say, without a trace of guilt,
So we go.
Passing the girl in the hall.
'Bye' I say frostily,
I suppose
You winked.

Georgia Garrett

Lost on the Common

From *The Prelude*

                                    I remember well,
That once, while yet my inexperienced hand
Could scarcely hold a bridle, with proud hopes
I mounted, and we journeyed towards the hills:
An ancient servant of my father's house
Was with me, my encourager and guide:
We had not travelled long, ere some mischance
Disjoined me from my comrade; and, through fear
Dismounting, down the rough and stony moor
I led my horse, and, stumbling on, at length
Came to a bottom, where in former times
A murderer had been hung in iron chains.
The gibbet-mast had mouldered down, the bones
And iron case were gone; but on the turf,
Hard by, soon after that fell deed was wrought,
Some unknown hand had carved the murderer's name.

The monumental letters were inscribed
In times long past; but still, from year to year,
By superstition of the neighbourhood,
The grass is cleared away, and to this hour
The characters are fresh and visible:
A casual glance had shown them, and I fled,
Faltering and faint, and ignorant of the road:
Then, reascending the bare common, saw
A naked pool that lay beneath the hills,
The beacon on the summit, and, more near,
A girl, who bore a pitcher on her head,
And seemed with difficult steps to force her way
Against the blowing wind. It was, in truth,
An ordinary sight; but I should need
Colours and words that are unknown to man,
To paint the visionary dreariness
Which, while I looked all round for my lost guide,
Invested moorland waste, and naked pool,
The beacon crowning the lone eminence,
The female and her garments vexed and tossed
By the strong wind.

William Wordsworth

Here is the Cathedral

            And here
Under the West Front Saints' crumbling features
The Roman Garrison bath-house is being unearthed
Out of the dried blood of the redland marl –
Splayed, bleeding in rain, like an accident,
Gaped-at, photographed, commented-on, and coddled
With waterproofs. Nobody knows what to think of it.

And here are plague burials, incidentals
Surprised by the excavation –
Amber skeletons in their wedding chambers,
Touching couples, modest husbands and wives,
Dazzled awake by this sudden rude afterlife,
Cleaned with toothbrushes tenderly as hurt mouths,
Fleshless handbones folded over stomachs
Which no longer exist, and for faces
Clods of rained-on breccia –

            And here
Under the tarmac brink, under headlamp chromes
Of Peugeots, Toyotas, Volkswagens, Jaguars, Saabs,
Spades have hacked an eight-foot vertical cliff
Through mediaeval solid bone-dump, skull-caps
Carried about by dogs, rib-struts, limb-strakes
Littering the redland mud, like trampled laths
At a demolition. And this is the House of the Dead,
Open to everybody.

            And here is the door
Of the Cathedral. Going in out of the rain
I met a dark figure in the doorway:

Shuffling on rotten feet in rotten shoes
The whuffling wino with simplified face
Outsize R.A.F. greatcoat, trailing tatters,
Dragged lower by the black unlabelled bottle
In his pocket, was asking for something. A whimper.
A paw red as if sore, oily and creased,
Muffled some request.

                    Cash for renovations –
A cup of tea and a sandwich.
My first tenpenny piece conjured voices.
All my loose change shattered the heights –
And two furious ones, with sparkling faces,
With fierce heavenly eyes, with Sunday suits,
Arrived in a glare of question.

                        One swayed
Crushing me with new worlds of consideration,
With angelic mouthfuls of sociology,
The other, pink-scrubbed, brass-eyed, Christian Knight,
Was butting at the wino with his chest,
Impeccable godly fists clenched at his seams
At attention, like a police horse at a crowd,
He bumped the faceless mop of boy-black hair,
The dwarf-swollen nose, the coat on two shabby boots –

'How many times do you have to be told – out!
We've told you, haven't we? You do know, don't you?
Then out! Get out! Get out and stay out!'

Huddling mouse in his cloth,
Goblin aboriginal under his hair mop
Shuffled and tottered out.

                  Flushed with the work
Glistening righteousness and staring image
Wrathful commissionaires
Whisked back into the heights
Among columns and arches –
Leaving me an expendable tortoise
Of the war in Heaven.

                Between masks
In rictus of sanctity, and the glossed slabs
Of the defunct.

            With whispers
Draining down from the roots of the hair – OUT

OUT OUT OUT

Ted Hughes

Decomposition

I have a picture I took in Bombay
of a beggar asleep on the pavement:
grey-haired, wearing shorts and a dirty shirt,
his shadow thrown aside like a blanket.

His arms and legs could be cracks in the stone,
routes for the ants' journeys, the flies' descents.
Brain-washed by the sun into exhaustion,
he lies veined into stone, a fossil man.

Behind him, there is a crowd passingly
bemused by a pavement trickster and quite
indifferent to this very common sight
of an old man asleep on the pavement.

I thought it then a good composition
and glibly called it *The Man in the Street*,
remarking how typical it was of
India that the man in the street lived there.

His head in the posture of one weeping
into a pillow chides me now for my
presumption at attempting to compose
art out of his hunger and solitude.

Zulfikar Ghose

Talk Talk Talk

Poetry doesn't make much sense to me until somebody reads it out loud. When you hear it read properly, the words fall into place. You see what they mean at last.

You can change the meaning of a poem simply by the way you say it, can't you?

Head of English

Today we have a poet in the class.
A real live poet with a published book.
Notice the inkstained fingers girls. Perhaps
we're going to witness verse hot from the press.
Who knows. Please show your appreciation
by clapping. Not too loud. Now

sit up straight and listen. Remember
the lesson on assonance, for not all poems,
sadly, rhyme these days. Still. Never mind.
Whispering's, as always, out of bounds –
but do feel free to raise some questions.
After all, we're paying forty pounds.

Those of you with English Second Language
see me after break. We're fortunate
to have this person in our midst.
Season of mists and so on and so forth.
I've written quite a bit of poetry myself,
am doing Kipling with the Lower Fourth.

Right. That's enough from me. On with the Muse.
Open a window at the back. We don't
want winds of change about the place.
Take notes, but don't write reams. Just an essay
on the poet's themes. Fine. Off we go.
Convince us that there's something we don't know.

Well. Really. Run along now girls. I'm sure
that gave an insight to an outside view.
Applause will do. Thank you
very much for coming here today. Lunch
in the hall? Do hang about. Unfortunately
I have to dash. Tracey will show you out.

Carol Anne Duffy

The Railway Clerk

It isn't my fault.
I do what I'm told
but still I am blamed.
This year, my leave application
was twice refused.
Every day there is so much work
and I don't get overtime.
My wife is always asking for more money.
Money, money, where to get money?
My job is such, no one is giving bribe,
while other clerks are in fortunate position,
and no promotion even because I am not graduate.

I wish I was bird.

I am never neglecting my responsibility,
I am discharging it properly,
I am doing my duty,
but who is appreciating?
Nobody, I am telling you.

My desk is too small,
the fan is not repaired for two months,
three months.
I am living far off in Borivli,
my children are neglecting studies,
how long this can go on?

Nissim Ezekial

You Will be Hearing From Us Shortly

You feel adequate to the demands of this position?
What qualities do you feel you
Personally have to offer?

                                        Ah

Let us consider your application form.
Your qualifications, though impressive, are
Not, we must admit, precisely what
We had in mind. Would you care
To defend their relevance?

                                        Indeed

Now your age. Perhaps you feel able
To make your own comment about that,
Too? We are conscious ourselves
Of the need for a candidate with precisely
The right degree of immaturity.

                                        So glad we agree

And now a delicate matter: your looks.
You do appreciate this work involves
Contact with the actual public? Might they,
Perhaps, find your appearance
Disturbing?

                                        Quite so

And your accent. That is the way
You have always spoken, is it? What
Of your education? Were
You educated? We mean, of course,
Where were you educated?

                   And how
Much of a handicap is that to you,
Would you say?

             Married, children.
We see. The usual dubious
Desire to perpetuate what had better
Not have happened at all. We do not
Ask what domestic disasters shimmer
Behind that vaguely unsuitable address.

And you were born –?

                               Yes. Pity.

So glad we agree.

U. A. Fanthorpe

Is You

A Caribbean Folk Tale

Ah walk de street de odder day;
Ah hea a man bawl an shout,
is I name him atek liberty wid:
'Gubba, Gubba, Gub.' Him acall to I
so me stop in I track, wonderin who know me so.

Tis long, long time now me astop use dat name;
ever since Ah did come to Hingland from back home
Ah use a different handle,
just like de Hinglish people dem.
First, mister, den I two Christian name;
den I surname, den a dash, den I odder surname.
After dat I put I title, ESQ, just like dat.
It does look good on a letter see.

So dis man him acome run-in up to I,
real hard foot, pantin' an out a bret,
breathin' fast fast.
'Gubba, Gubba, is you, is you,' him sey.
Grabbin' I by I hand, but me apull way
an pretend not fe know him.
'Awful sorry old chap, but I'm afraid you're somewhat
    mistaken.'
Me atell him in Hinglish voice:
not Cockney, but in oxbridge accent,
like me had hot patato in I mout.
Ya see a does tek off de voices dem.

Well him adraw back an peer up in I face.
'Is you, is you,' him sey. 'Me not forget notin:
me know you face anywhere.
Is thief I an you athief togedder wen we was back home.'

Well ya can imagine I consternation –
nice word dat eh?
Dere me was, dressed up fit fe kill
in I best Sunday go-to-meetin' suit. Only it was Wednesday.
An ah had dis gal wid I.

Hinglish gal dat, posh voice an money to burn,
real middle class.

An along come dis *bugg-ah-boo man*, talkin like so:
'Is you, is you.' An tellin she
me use fe thief an ting wid he.
But is big lie him alie ya know.
I not thief notin wid he.
Though him really know I; we was like so back home,
wen we was lil *pickney* an ting an ever later.
But boy now is pretend I really hav fe pretend, like mad.
Cause de bugg-ah-boo man out fe shame I.

De act me put on me deserve a oscar fe it.
Listen now, de big mout man him astart fe tell
de gal one story, bout me. Big story dis ya know,
full a lie an ting; an de gal alisten to he.
Ya no wha dem liberal white Hinglish gal like.
Dem sa polite to black men dem. Boy!
None a dem will tell ya g'away, to ya face.
Not like de black sister dem. No sir:
now-ah-days dem real fancy ya see. Boy!
Ya should see dem. Dem not give way notin', no more.
Dat's why de Hinglish gal ascore pun dem;
dem not free an easy again. Boy! Hey!
De table really turn, eh?

Hanyway de old bugg-ah-boo alick him mout faster dan
de politician dem, ina election year.
De big mout atell de gal some real bad bad tings
bout me, like so:
me ain't went to school,
I father had ten children an no wife,
me stow way pun banana boat,
me can't spell cat from bull-foot,
all de Chinee children call me daddy,
me after her money, me tell him bout her:
an a lot more bad bad ting him talk.

Sa me hav fe tell she fe ignore he,
cause some black people dem so – jealous an ting –
hallways atry fee lowrate dem fella black man,
wen dem see ya doin' better dan dem.
Den me tek she by she hand and carry she way.
Hey, ya should asee we put foot pun ground,
high steppin' out a dere, lickety-split.
But boy! De bugg-ah-boo man him afollow we,
bawlin' all de time, nough fe wake de dead.
'Is you! Is you!' Him acall after we.
Man a tell ya, ya should asee he.

Jimi Rand

When You Are Old

It's interesting to read about old people because so much more has happened to them. I listen to my grandmother even though she repeats things because I know that she will not be there forever. I want to preserve something of her in my memory.

It's not the getting old that people fear, it's the not being able to do things for yourself.

*C*rabbed Age

Crabbed age and youth cannot live together,
Youth is full of pleasance, Age is full of care,
Youth like summer morne, Age like winter weather,
Youth like summer brave, Age like winter bare.
Youth is full of sport, Ages breath is short,
Youth is nimble, Age is lame
Youth is hot and bold, Age is weake and cold,
Youth is wild, and Age is tame.
   Age I doe abhor thee, Youth I doe adore thee,
     O my love my love is young:
   Age I doe defie thee. Oh sweet Shepheard hie thee:
     For me thinks thou staies too long.

William Shakespeare

On Aging

When you see me sitting quietly,
Like a sack left on the shelf,
Don't think I need your chattering.
I'm listening to myself.
Hold! Stop! Don't pity me!
Hold! Stop your sympathy!
Understanding if you got it,
Otherwise I'll do without it!

When my bones are stiff and aching
And my feet won't climb the stair,
I will only ask one favor:
Don't bring me no rocking chair.

When you see me walking, stumbling,
Don't study and get it wrong.
'Cause tired don't mean lazy
And every goodbye ain't gone.
I'm the same person I was back then,
A little less hair, a little less chin,
A lot less lungs and much less wind.
But ain't I lucky I can still breathe in.

Maya Angelou

Note for the Future

When I get old
don't dress me in
frayed jackets
and too-short trousers,
and send me out
to sit around bowling-greens
in summer.
Don't give me just enough
to exist on, and expect me
to like passing
the winter days
in the reading-room
of the local library, waiting
my turn to read
last night's local paper.
Shoot me!
Find a reason, any reason,
say I'm a troublemaker,
or can't take care of myself
and live in a dirty room.
If you're afraid
of justifying my execution
on those terms,
tell everyone I leer
at little girls, and then
shoot me!
I don't care why you do it,
but do it,
and don't leave me
to walk to corner-shops
counting my coppers,
or give me a pass to travel cheap
at certain times, like a leper.

Jim Burns

Never

It never went right –
there was always something:
she couldn't stand her father because he smoked a pipe,
her mother embarrassed her because she broke wind in public,
her older sister had the best room,
her younger brother was always top of his class at school,
her husband never got promoted as he should have done
and when he died prematurely, her pension was barely adequate
and then her daughter married someone she couldn't stand
and for years she's had this pain behind her left ear and
    something in her right leg and under her shoulderblades and
    a terrible itch in her crotch that wakens her at two in the
    morning
and a long list of foods (and medicines) that she can't stand
    (no end of people or things she can't stand)
and . . . and . . . and . . . and now
she's got this peculiar sensation in her stomach that turns out
    to be a cancer but too far gone to be removed and they've
    sent her home to die
and quite literally she can't stand any more
and her sister-in-law is looking after her very patiently
    (particulary since she doesn't speak to her brother)
and she's seventy-nine
and the old gentleman next door (who used to do her
    shopping for her) has accidentally backed his car over a
    corner of her lawn . . .
it never went right –
there was always something.

Gael Turnbull

Grandmother

By the time I knew my grandmother she was dead.
Before that she was where I thought she stood,
Spectacles, slippers, venerable head,
A standard-issue twinkle in her eyes –
Familiar stage-props of grandmotherhood.
It took her death to teach me they were lies.

My sixteen-year-old knowingness was shocked
To hear her family narrate her past
In quiet nostalgic chorus. As they talked
Her body stiffened on the muted fast
Though well washed linen coverlet of her bed.
The kitchen where we sat, a room I knew,
Took on a strangeness with each word they said.
How she was born where wealth was pennies, grew
Into a woman before she was a girl,
From dirt and pain constructed happiness,
Shed youth's dreams in the fierce sweat of a mill,
Married and mothered in her sixteenth year,
Fed children from her own mouth's emptiness
In an attic rats owned half of, liked her beer.
Careless, they scattered pictures: mother, wife,
Strikes lived through, hard concessions bought and sold
In a level-headed bargaining with life,
Told anecdotes in which her strength rang gold,
Her eyes were clear, her wants as plain as salt.
The past became a mint from which they struck
Small change till that room glittered like a vault.
The corpse in the other room became to me
Awesome as Pharaoh now, as if one look
Would show me all that I had failed to see.

The kitchen became museum in my sight,
Sacred as church. These were the very chairs
In which her gnarled dignity grew frail.
Her hard-won pride had kept these brasses bright.
Her tireless errands were etched upon the stairs.
A vase shone in the sun, holy as grail.

I wanted to bring others to this room,
Say it's nothing else than this that people mean,
A place to which humility can come,
A wrested niche where no one else has been
Won from the wastes of broken worlds and worse.
Here we can stay. Stupid and false, of course.
Themselves to the living is all we have to give.

Let this be
To her, for wreath, gift, true apology.

William McIlvanney

For My Grandmother Knitting

There is no need they say
but the needles still move
their rhythms in the working of your hands
as easily
as if your hands
were once again those sure and skilful hands
of the fisher-girl.

You are old now
and your grasp of things is not so good
but master of your moments then
deft and swift
you slit the still-ticking quick silver fish.
Hard work it was too
of necessity.

But now they say there is no need
as the needles move
in the working of your hands
once the hands of the bride
with the hand-span waist
once the hands of the miner's wife
who scrubbed his back
in a tin bath by the coal fire
once the hands of the mother
of six who made do and mended
scraped and slaved slapped sometimes
when necessary.

But now they say there is no need
the kids they say grandma
have too much already
more than they can wear
too many scarves and cardigans –
gran you do too much
there's no necessity.

At your window you wave
them goodbye Sunday.
With your painful hands
big on shrunken wrists.
Swollen-jointed. Red. Arthritic. Old.
But the needles still move
their rhythms in the working of your hands
easily
as if your hands remembered
of their own accord the pattern
as if your hands had forgotten
how to stop.

Liz Lochhead

Grandfather

They brought him in on a stretcher from the world,
Wounded but humorous. And he soon recovered.
Boiler-rooms, row upon row of gantries rolled
Away to reveal the landscape of a childhood
Only he can recapture. Even on cold
Mornings he is up at six with a block of wood
Or a box of nails, discreetly up to no good
Or banging round the house like a four-year-old –

Never there when you call. But after dark
You hear his great boots thumping in the hall
And in he comes, as cute as they come. Each night
His shrewd eyes bolt the door and set the clock
Against the future, then his light goes out.
Nothing escapes him; he escapes us all.

Derek Mahon

Leave-taking

The only joy
of his old age
he often said
was his grandson

Their friendship
straddled
eight decades
three generations

They laughed, played
quarrelled, embraced
watched television together
and while the rest had
little to say to the old man
the little fellow was
a fountain of endless chatter

When death rattled
the gate at five
one Sunday morning
took the old man away
others trumpeted their
grief in loud sobs
and lachrymose blubber

He never shed a tear
just waved one of his
small inimitable goodbyes
to his grandfather
and was sad the old man
could not return his gesture.

Cecil Rajendra

Part Three
To be Continued

*I*deas for Further Thinking, Talking and Writing

This final section of the book gives further ideas about how poetry can be approached.

The first six activities here are offered as general techniques for approaching poetry, although each of them is grounded in specific examples. The rest of the activities relate to particular poems or sections.

Making Comparisons

This anthology begins with a section of paired poems which can be compared with each other. If you have found that having poems to contrast one with another makes writing about them easier, you may like to look at some of these connections.

Comparing Poems Through Statements

A simple and effective way of beginning to compare two poems is by looking at the statements other people have made about them.

Five or six opinions are enough with which to make a start. For example, look at these opinions about *Gangrene* by Taufiq Rafat and *'Out, Out–'* by Robert Frost:

a What makes me angry in both poems is the attitude of adults.

b I think the tragedy is worse in *'Out, Out–'*, because it happens so suddenly: a moment's carelessness.

c *Gangrene* is the poem that upset me more because of the effect of their superstition.

d There is more story to *Gangrene* and that is why I think it is more effective.

e I like the fact that *'Out, Out–'* gives you some of the boy's own reaction. You don't get that in *Gangrene*.

f The thing that makes *Gangrene* work as a narrative poem is the fact that it is told by someone who is involved in the story.

Group/Individual Work

Which statement comes closest to your own feeling about the poem?

Try to rank the statements in order of their usefulness as comments about the poems.

Are there any statements with which you disagree? Why?

Assignment

Use your reactions to the poems and to the statements as a basis for a piece of writing about them.

The Poem I Prefer

When you are planning to talk or write about your preference for one poem rather than another, it often helps to have a structure for your thinking. You may be able to think up your own method, but here is one way of doing this.

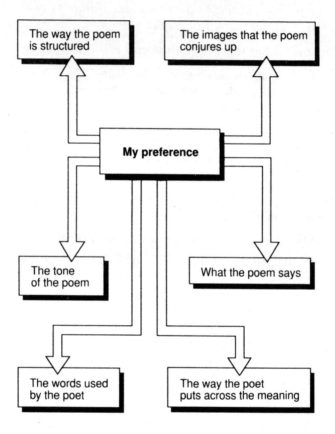

Poetry Survey

One way of becoming clearer in your own mind about the way a poem works is to compare your thoughts with several other people's reactions.

If you do this you will need to listen very carefully and take full notes about what they say. You may find it useful to use a tape recorder, if one is available.

Once you have collected several views, you can summarize them and set them alongside your own. It is not always easy but it is interesting to consider why people's responses differ.

A Survey of Humorous Poetry

Let the people in your survey read the section *Not So Serious* (or, at least, several poems in that section). Ask them:
 Which poem did you like best? Why?
 What was your favourite line?
 Which poem did you like least? Why?

Other Surveys

You might choose any of the themes in this anthology or you might make a grouping of three or four poems that interest you.

Do not create too large a group of poems and do not ask too many questions: three or four poems and three or four questions will create a survey that takes quite a long time to complete even if you only speak to half a dozen people properly.

Hot Seating

Hot seating means that characters from poems, or the poets themselves, are placed in front of a group who can then cross question them. The character or the poet is thus placed 'in the hot seat'.

At its best, this is one of the liveliest and most interesting ways of finding out about a poem.

Two aspects need careful preparation. Firstly a person who is going to be in the hot seat needs to know the poem inside out. Second, people who are going to ask the questions need to have their material well prepared.

On the first occasion it may well be the teacher who takes the part of the character in the hot seat with four or five pupils chosen to do the questioning. As the technique becomes familiar, the whole of the class may be involved, split into several groups.

Some possibilities for hot seating:

Ted Hughes in *A Knock at the Door*.
The tramp in *A Knock at the Door*.
The boy's father in *Gangrene*.
Noah in *Saturday Sailor*.
The teacher in *To a Crippled Schoolmaster*.
Great Grandfather in *Great Grandfather's Bridge*.
Alice Walker in both her poems.
Maki Kureishi in *Kittens*.
Seamus Heaney in *Death of a Naturalist*.
Ben Hall's friend in *The Death of Ben Hall*.
Mary Cummings in Alan Bold's poem.
Tommy in *In the Children's Hospital*.
The veteran in Margaret Postgate Cole's poem.
Uncle Bert in Robert Morgan's poem.
Carole Satyamurti in *Broken Moon*.
The attendants in *Here is the Cathedral*.
The poet in *Head of English*.
The wife in *The Railway Clerk*.

Making an Anthology

One way of presenting your preferences in poetry is to create your own anthology based around themes or individual writers.

The way you present your anthology is largely up to you.

You might choose to put the whole of a particular poem in your anthology, or only a part of it. It makes sense to be selective, because no one is impressed by sheer volume.

When you have made a choice, accompany it by a few sentences which explain why you have chosen a particular poem. If you are preparing this for an assessment, remember that the most important part of your anthology is what you yourself say about the poems.

A Love Anthology

One of the most common themes in poetry is love. One section of this anthology – *Love More or Less* – is composed entirely of poems about love's success or failure. In addition there are a wide variety of poems in other parts of the anthology which comment on love or lack of it. Ones that you could look at might include:

Waiting for Thelma's Laughter   *Grace Nichols*
My Uncle E.P.M. Harawa   *Felix Mnthali*
Poem at Thirty-Nine *Alice Walker*
For My Sister Molly Who in the Fifties   *Alice Walker*
Mary Cummings   *Alan Bold*
The Horse That Had a Flat Tire   *Richard Brautigan*
Broken Moon   *Carole Satyamurti*
The Song of Wandering Aengus   *W.B. Yeats*
Incident   *Fleur Adcock*
Manwatching   *Georgia Garrett*

Apart from what you can find in this book, almost any poetry anthology will have poems on love for you to think about.

Other Anthologies

Students have produced anthologies on a wide range of topics. Here are just a few:

The State of the World
Animal Poetry
West Indian Poetry
Ballads
Three Women Writers
Poetry from Prison

If you choose to produce an anthology, do not forget it is your reactions and thoughts that matter, not just the selection of the poems.

Getting to Grips with a Poem

One of the most tried and tested ways of getting to know a poem better is to make notes in pencil on and around the poem itself. Using pencil allows you to make alterations, if you change your mind. It is a good idea to make a copy of the poem in question so that you do not need to mark the book itself.

Here are the responses one student made to *Animals* by Walt Whitman.

turn where?
(away from people ??)

1st sentence
makes you
think

anti
religion ??

not bothered
about guilt

I think I could turn and live with animals, they are so placid
    and self-contained;
I stand and look at them long and long. ← —— odd phrase
They do not sweat and whine about their condition;
They do not lie awake in the dark and weep for their sins;

They do not make me sick discussing their duty to God;
Not one is dissatisfied – not one is demented with the mania of
    owning things;

Not one kneels to another, nor to his kind that lived thousands
    of years ago;

Not one is respectable or industrious over the whole earth.

who are these?

no
dressing
up

no people
in power,
no upper class

they get what they
need but they don't
go on and on working
(I think !)

134

Notice that the responses include a variety of things:

thoughts about what words mean
questions about parts not understood
comments on phrases/ideas/words
possible explanations.

After you have made some notes, it is worth sharing your ideas with another member of your group. If you have been working on the same poem you will be able to compare responses, and perhaps clear up each other's doubts about the poem's meaning and purpose.

Suggested Poems

Almost any poetry can be approached in this way but the following are some suggestions as to where you might like to start:

First Love   *John Clare*
The Parting   *Michael Drayton*
The Horse That Had a Flat Tire   *Richard Brautigan*
Broken Moon   *Carole Satyamurti*
Incident   *Fleur Adcock*
Lost on the Common   *William Wordsworth*

Suggestions for Particular Poems and Sections

A Knock at the Door (page 12)

Imagine that what has occurred in this poem, happened to you. Back inside, your younger brother asks you who it was and what they wanted.

Write out the conversation in which you describe the tramp's call, what he looked like, what he wanted and what your reaction was.

If you are working as a class, you may choose to start by hot seating either the tramp or Ted Hughes (see page 131).

The Contract (page 19)

Prepare an advertisement for life based on Norman Nicholson's poem.

You will need to decide whether the small print at the bottom is large enough to be read or not.

The Collier (page 24)
Saturday Sailor (page 26)

If you are not familiar with the stories of Joseph and Noah, you will need to find out about them in order to understand and appreciate these two poems.

What do you think about the way these poets have used and adapted the original stories?

Try to imagine the conversation of the miners trapped in the pit or the gossip when Noah begins to build his boat.

Gangrene (page 28)

Imagine that the boy's father is explaining to one of his cousins what happened to his son. What would he say?

If you are working as a class, you may wish to use hot seating here (see page 131).

My Kind of People (page 33)

a Which of the people described in these poems would you most like to meet? Why?

You might find it helpful to think about:
who they were
what they achieved
why they were admired.

b What differences can you see in the way that the poets show their appreciation? You might want to think about:

the tone of the poem
the details that the poet records
the style of the poem
the way in which the poem is divided
the overall impression.

c Choose one of these poems as a pattern for your own writing about someone you admire.

Able (page 45)

a The first poem in this section is called *Does It Matter?* Think and write about the different ways in which the poets show how disabilities matter.

You may find it helpful to look at *Getting to Grips with a Poem* on page 134.

b The narrators of these poems each have a different position and perspective.

See if you can describe who they are and how they feel about the subject. Which narrator do you think is most effective?

Creatures (page 53)

a Think about the characters of the animals described in these poems and write a few sentences about how you imagine each of them. Your work might begin like this:

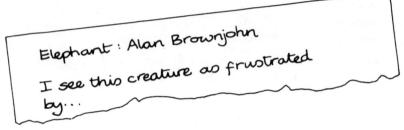

Elephant : Alan Brownjohn
I see this creature as frustrated
by...

When you have written about each of the animals' characters, choose one of them and imagine what they might like to say if they were given a chance.
Alan Brownjohn's poem will give you some ideas about how you could write this.

b If you had to choose just two of the poems to represent the way that people respond to animals, which ones would they be? Can you defend your choice?

Story (page 61)

a Imagine the talk in the bar when Ben Hall's traitorous friend is no longer there. Include in your scene a character who is new to the area, who knows very little of Ben Hall's story and asks to hear more.

You might choose to set this out in play form.

b Think about Mary Cummings' situation. Why is she in prison? What is about to happen to her?

When you feel confident about your answers, try preparing a report for the local newspaper about her. If you are working as a class, hot seating the character is one way in which you could begin your thinking here (see page 131).

c What differences do you notice between the two traditional ballads (*The Death of Ben Hall* and *The Daemon Lover*) and the two more modern ones (*The Ballad of Charlotte Dymond* and *Mary Cummings*)?

d It is quite common for parts of a story to be left unexplained in a ballad. What mysteries remain after you have read these poems? How would you explain those mysteries?

Love More or Less (page 73)

See under *Making an Anthology* on page 132.

Not So Serious (page 83)

See under *Poetry Survey* on page 131.

Prejudiced (page 91)

a Even when A.E. Houseman was writing, no one was actually punished for the colour of their hair. What kind of things are people condemned for, which are not their own fault?

b Think about the prejudices that Juanita Bell meets about Indian children. Do people say similar things about other groups?

c In Carole Satyamurti's poem, it is an individual – her father – who has been victimized. What happened to her father and what happens today?

d Write about the way that these poems have made you think again about prejudice. If you want to express a preference for one particular poem you may find that the section *The Poem I Prefer* on page 130 is useful.

Mysteries

(page 95)

If you were preparing a video to accompany the words of one
or more of these poems, what would you want to include?

You will need to think about the settings, any characters to
be included and any action that your cameras will capture. Your
script for filming might begin like this:

The Tide Rises, the Tide Falls

Scene 1. Beach

Camera passes from view
of beach and lingers on
the shoreline as the
waves come and go.

Camera swings around to
capture the darkening
cliff face.

VOICE: The tide rises,
the tide falls,

VOICE: The twilight
darkens, the curlew
calls;

Moments in Time

(page 101)

Take one or more of these incidents and try to tell it from
another point of view.

For example, if you chose to be the boyfriend in
Manwatching, you might think about some of these questions:

Why am I watching the other girl?
What do I think of the other girl's response?
How do I expect my girlfriend to react?
What do I feel about the way she actually reacts?
What do I think about the party generally?
What do I feel about my relationship with my girlfriend?

You may find hot seating useful here. See page 131.

Talk Talk Talk (page 109)

a Prepare production notes for a dramatized performance of one of these poems. You will need to answer the following questions before you begin:

How many voices would you use?
What accents would be helpful?
What tone is needed?
What else would help a performance?

b If you were the visiting poet in *Head of English*, how would you describe your visit when you got home?

You may imagine you are talking to your husband/son/daughter/friend/next door neighbour. Remember that what you say will be affected by whom you are saying it to.

c See if you can write a poem in a similar style to *The Railway Clerk*, called *The Railway Clerk's Wife*.

How might her view of the situation be different?
If you are working as a class, you might find hot seating helpful for this and for the previous suggestion. See page 131.

d Try to tell a story, in as lively a way as Jimi Rand does, about meeting an old ex-friend you would rather forget. Use any dialect that is familiar to you.

When You Are Old (page 117)

a If you were preparing a campaign designed to improve attitudes to old people, which of these poems would you use and why? Which ones would you avoid?

Prepare some general notes about your campaign and how you might use poetry. Give a more detailed idea about how you would use one particular poem, for example, as part of a leaflet or poster.

b Compare *On Aging* and *Note for the Future*. Which do you prefer? Why?

You may find it helpful to look at the suggestions for thinking about contrasting poems on page 128.

Acknowledgements

The editor and publisher are grateful for permission to include the following copyright poems:

Fleur Adcock, 'Incident' from *Selected Poems*, © Fleur Adcock 1983. Reprinted by permission of Oxford University Press. **Maya Angelou**, 'On Aging' and 'The Lie' from *And Still I Rise* (1985). Reprinted by permission of Virago Press. **Patricia Beer**, 'The Fifth Sense'. Reprinted by permission of the author. **Juanita Bell**, 'Indian Children Speak' published in *From the Belly of the Shark*, ed. Walter Lowenfels (1973), reprinted in *Poetry, An Introduction*, ed. Ruth Miller and Walter Greenberg (St Martin's Press, 1981) © Marna Lowenfels-Perpelitt. **Alan Bold**, 'Mary Cummings' © Alan Bold 1982. Reprinted by permission of the author. **Richard Brautigan**, 'The Horse That Had a Flat Tire' © Richard Brautigan 1968, from *The Pill Versus the Springhill Mine Disaster*. Reprinted by permission of The Helen Brann Agency, Inc. **Alan Brownjohn**, 'Elephant' from *Brownjohn's Bestiary*. Reprinted by permission of the author. **Jim Burns**, 'Note for the Future' reprinted in *Strictly Private*, ed. Roger McGough. © Jim Burns. **Charles Causley**, 'The Ballad of Charlotte Dymond' from *Collected Poems* (Macmillan). Reprinted by permission of David Higham Associates Ltd. **Carol Anne Duffy**, 'Head of English' from *Standing Female Nude*. Reprinted by permission of Anvil Press Poetry Ltd. **Nissim Ezekial**, 'The Railway Clerk' from *Hymns in Darkness* (1976). Reprinted by permission of Oxford University Press, Delhi. **U. A. Fanthorpe**, 'You Will be Hearing From Us Shortly' from *Standing To* (Peterloo Poets, 1982) and *Selected Poems* (Peterloo Poets & King Penguin, 1986). Used with permission. **Robert Frost**, 'Out, Out–' from *The Poetry of Robert Frost*, ed. Edward Connery Lathem. Reprinted by permission of Jonathan Cape on behalf of the Estate of Robert Frost. **Georgia Garrett**, 'Manwatching' published in *I See a Voice*, ed. Michael Rosen (1982). © Georgia Garrett. **Zulfikar Ghose**, 'Decomposition' from *Jets From Orange* (Macmillan, London, 1967), © Zulfikar Ghose 1967. Reprinted by permission of the author. **Martyn Halsall**, 'Saturday Sailor' © Martyn Halsall 1978. Reprinted by permission of the author. **Seamus Heaney**, 'Death of a Naturalist' from *Death of Naturalist*. Reprinted by permission of Faber & Faber Ltd. **Ted Hughes**, ' A Knock at the Door' and 'Here is the Cathedral' from *Moortown*. Reprinted by permission of Faber & Faber Ltd. **Erica Jong**, 'There is Only One Story' from *Ordinary Miracles* © Erica Jong 1983. Reprinted by permission of Sterling Lord Literistic, Inc. **Arun Kolatkar**, 'An Old Woman' reprinted in *Ten Twentieth Century Indian Poets*, ed. R. Parthasarathy (O.U.P. Delhi, 1976.) © Arun Kolatkar 1976. **Maki Kureishi**, 'Kittens' fron *Wordfall* ed. Kaleem Omar (O.U.P. Karachi).

Reprinted by permission of O.U.P. Karachi. **Fran Landesman**, 'The Tigers of Pain' from *Is It Overcrowded in Heaven?*, Golden Handshake, 8 Duncan Terrace, London N1, England. Used with permission. **Liz Lochhead**, 'For My Grandmother Knitting' from *Dreaming Frankenstein*. Reprinted by permission of Polygon. **George Macbeth**, 'One Gone, Eight to Go' from *Poem from Oby*, © George Macbeth 1982. Reprinted by permission of Martin Secker & Warburg Ltd. **Hugh MacDiarmid**, 'In the Children's Hospital' from *The Complete Poems*. Reprinted by permission of Martin, Brian & O'Keeffe Ltd. **Roger McGough**, 'The Lake' from Selected Poems. Reprinted by permission of Jonathan Cape on behalf of the author. **William McIlvanney**, 'Grandmother' from *The Longships in Harbour* (Eyre & Spottiswoode). Reprinted by permission of Curtis Brown Group Ltd. **Derek Mahon**, 'Grandfather' from *Poems 1962–1978*, © Derek Mahon 1979. Reprinted by permission of Oxford University Press. **Felix Mnthali**, 'My Uncle E.P.M. Harawa' from *When Sunset Comes to Sapitwa* (1982, Longman Group UK Ltd.), © Felix Mnthali 1982. Reprinted by permission of the publisher. **Robert Morgan**, 'Uncle Bert', © Robert Morgan 1986. Reprinted by permission of the author c/o Campbell Thomson & McLaughlin Ltd. **Mervyn Morris**, 'To a Crippled Schoolmaster' from *The Pond* by Mervyn Morris (New Beacon Books, 1973). Reprinted by permission of the publisher. **Grace Nichols**, 'Waiting for Thelma's Laughter' from *The Fat Black Woman's Poems* (1984). Reprinted by permission of Virago Press. **Norman Nicholson**, 'The Contract', © Norman Nicholson 1987. Reprinted by permission of David Higham Associates Ltd. **Kaleem Omar**, 'Great Grandfather's Bridge' from *Wordfall*, ed. Kaleem Omar (O.U.P. Karachi). Reprinted by permission of O.U.P. Karachi. **Ian Parks**, 'A Dream of Snow' published in *Footnotes* Magazine, Edition 3, by the Schools' Poetry Association. © Ian Parks. **Brian Patten**, 'The Newcomer' © Brian Patten, from *Gargling with Jelly* (Viking Kestrel Books, 1985). **Marge Piercy**, 'Cold Head, Cold Heart', from *My Mother's Body*. © Marge Piercy 1985. Rreprinted by kind permission of Unwin Hyman Ltd. **Peter Porter**, 'A Consumer's Report' from *Collected Poems*, © Peter Porter 1983. Reprinted by permission of Oxford University Press. **Margaret Postgate**, later **Cole**, 'The Veteran'. Reprinted by permission of H.J.D. Cole. **Taufiq Rafat**, 'Gangrene' from *Wordfall*, ed. Kaleem Omar (O.U.P. Karachi). Reprinted by permission of O.U.P. Karachi. **Jimi Rand**, 'Is You' from *Bluefoot Traveller*, ed. James Berry. © Jimi Rand 1985. **Irina Ratushinskaya**, 'I Had a Strange Dream' from *No, I'm Not Afraid* (1986). Reprinted by permission of Bloodaxe Books Ltd. **Cecil Rajendra**, 'Leave-taking' from *Hours of Assassins and Other Poems*. Reprinted by permission of Bogle-L'Ouverture Publications Ltd. **Siegfried Sassoon**, 'Does it Matter?'. Reprinted by permission of G.T. Sassoon. **Carole Satyamurti**,

The illustrations are by:
Alan Marks: p 15, pp 16–17, pp 26–27, p 59, p 85, p 98, p 120;
Jane Smith: p 21, p 39, pp 50–51, pp 54–55, p 71, p 76, p 82,
pp 112–113, p 115;
Martin White: p 41, p 46, p 62, p 89, p 96, pp 104–5, p 123.